HEALTH IS FOR PEOPLE

Health is for People

MICHAEL WILSON

Darton, Longman & Todd Ltd

First published in Great Britain in 1975 by
Darton, Longman & Todd Ltd
89 Lillie Road, London SW6 1UD

© Michael Wilson, 1975

ISBN 0 232 51326 0

Printed in Great Britain by litho at The Anchor Press Ltd
and bound by Wm Brendon & Son Ltd
both of Tiptree, Essex

Reprinted 1976
Reprinted 1977

To
Susan, Christopher, Timothy, Francis,
Mark, David, Jennifer
and their generation

Contents

viii

Preface

In 1971 I wrote a research study entitled *The Hospital—a Place of Truth*. This present book is written in order to explore further one of the most important questions in that study—What is health? It is a book for all readers because health concerns everyone: there are no specialists in health.

When I first set out to find a publisher for this book I was told that no publisher was likely to accept it because the subject material was difficult for a bookseller to classify. Fortunately I have found a publisher willing to take the risk. . . . But what can I say to the bookseller?

You could without difficulty place it among the books on medicine, social work, theology, psychology, ethics, politics, care of the environment, human behaviour . . . and the book would be equally comfortable/uncomfortable among its neighbours. But that is one point of this book. Health has been claimed for the medical shelf too long, and it is time that it was spread around more widely. Please put the book in several different disciplines, for there are few corners of knowledge which will be entirely alien to one of the greatest unifying ideas in human life—health.

I wish to thank the Trustees of the Joseph Rowntree Charitable Trust who financed my research fellowship in the University of Birmingham and made this further book possible.

I am indebted to three friends especially from whose conversation, writing and encouragement I have gained constant inspiration: the late Dr. R. A. Lambourne, Dr. James Mathers and the late Rev. Canon R. E. C. Browne. In particular I wish to thank the two last-mentioned friends and my son Christopher J. Wilson, for reading and criticising the original draft and for making valuable suggestions.

Other friends and colleagues, doctors, nurses, patients and students have helped to shape the ideas in this book.

I also wish to thank my wife Jean who has contributed much from her own experience. She typed all the manuscripts, and shared the whole project.

M.W.

NOTES

(i) Throughout the book—for the sake of convenience—the male gender is used, it could equally well have been the female: there is no sex (or colour, or national) discrimination in health.

(ii) Quotations from the Old and New Testaments are from the *New English Bible* (Oxford University Press, Cambridge University Press), 1970

PART I

Health is Dead

DISEASE

In his novel *Nineteen Eighty Four* George Orwell[1] describes four ministries through which 'The Party' holds power: A Ministry of Peace concerned with war. A Ministry of Love for law and order. A Ministry of Plenty to deal with scarcities. A Ministry of Truth where a vast system of brain washing is planned and executed. He did not need to describe a Ministry of Health which deals with disease: we already have one.

In Great Britain our understanding of health is based on our knowledge of illness. We have the curious situation that the professions concerned with health (led by doctors) are primarily interested in disease. The institutions in the Health Service (particularly General Teaching Hospitals where new members of the professions are trained) are founded upon the same idea— that health is obtained by getting rid of disease.

It is difficult in Western society to talk about health without talking about disease.

Traditionally doctors have been trained to treat disease, and only comparatively recently has the understanding of causation become sufficient for thoughts to be drawn positively towards prevention and in turn towards the desire for positive health. Positive health, both physical and mental, implies care and understanding on the part of the individual. It has become clear that many of the diseases prevalent today are to a large extent attributable to modern ways of life, including such factors as cigarette smoking, overeating and lack of exercise . . .[2]

An attempt is made to speak about positive health, but at once the writer is trapped into speaking about diseases and bad habits. This is the way we think, and it is difficult to find words for a new description of health.

Our model of health is a medical one. It is also individualistic. We assume that health is an ideal state of human life in which all illness and handicap have been eliminated from each and every individual. We seek health by the prevention, diagnosis and treatment of disease in individual patients.

If we become aware that we are describing health in this negative way, it is usual to go on to say that obviously health is more than this: health is a positive quality of well-being. But it is difficult to describe what we mean by well-being without asking the question: What is health for?

In the army soldiers are classified as *fit* in relation to the tasks which they may have to do. Thus a man with flat feet is classified fit to drive a truck or build bridges, but he may not be fit for a march of twenty-five miles across rough country. A man with poor hearing is fit for clerical work, but not for night patrols. The use of the word *fitness* is related to the notion of a task to be done—fitness for the job. But it is difficult to use the word *health* in this way, unless we introduce the idea of being 'healthy *enough*' to do certain things. This would mean that health was not just perfection, but a practical notion related to function. We may be defective but we are healthy enough for a certain purpose. The army is more interested in what we can do than what we cannot do.

The National 'Health' Service is a disease prevention and cure service. Sources of dirt and disease are guarded against in food and water: poliomyelitis and smallpox can be prevented: cervical cancer can be foreseen. Treatment and advice are generally sought in times of sickness and crisis. The deterioration in old age is dealt with as a series of objectified problems— loneliness, meals, cutting of toe-nails—you name it, we have it, a whole range of valuable services.

Systems of health care have now become so complex that the word health is being given adjectives to try and hold it together.

My aim in making these proposals is to secure that the total health needs of each individual patient and each family will be met by one integrated health service . . . will enable everyone working at every level of the health service to plan, administer and provide for the comprehensive health needs of every citizen.[3]

Described in this way, a Health and Social Service is composed of an ever-expanding number of professions, disciplines and services which must be gathered into constellations and galaxies to deal with defects and problems as they arise in individuals and in groups. It then becomes increasingly difficult, in a problem family for example, to know whether the marriage guidance counsellor, the child guidance clinic, the probation service, the mental health welfare officer, the housing department, the school-teacher, the general practitioner, the local vicar—or all of them falling over one another—can best help. To deal with the whole situation a group of professionals is employed. Hence the need to speak of total, integrated and comprehensive health. But one wonders how far such a multiplicity of services is really concerned with the quality of life as a whole, or simply with bits and pieces of people's lives. And sometimes the woman who keeps the corner shop can help better than anyone.

Part of this complexity arises from the relationship between the Health and Social Services whose professions have important similarities to and differences from one another. On the one hand, the clinical approach of doctors and the casework method of social workers have important attitudes and principles in common. On the other hand social workers are more aware than doctors of the social dimensions of illness. This makes them sensitive to the political implications of their work in a sick society. The relevance of this to the training of a truly general practitioner is discussed below (page 99).

Members of some professions, for example clergy, avoid using the word health because they feel that the word lacks some content which could better be described by the word '*wholeness*'. Doctors and nurses may speak of 'whole person medicine', or of 'caring for the whole person'. The use of the word 'whole' is a protest against considering the body apart from the patient, or considering an individual patient in isolation from his family, or a family in isolation from the social conditions which make people well or ill.

The word *wellness* will be used as the opposite of illness, to describe the condition of not being ill. A doctor can examine a person and within the limits of his skill and equipment can say 'He is ill' or 'He is well'.* If he goes on to extend his examination by using a microscope or an X-ray machine he can say, again within the limits of his skill and equipment, 'He is ill' or 'He is well'. The word *wellness* is a clinical word, it describes the condition of not being ill (non-illness) within the doctor's knowledge of disease and the limits of his detective work. The word wellness, perhaps, comes nearest to the meaning of 'health' as we now use the word in Great Britain.

The way we speak about 'health' has important practical consequences. It is our understanding of health which shapes the design of a Health Centre (see page 92), the structure of the National Health Service and the kind of training we give to doctors and nurses.

A SANITATED SOCIETY

There are many illnesses and handicaps about which doctors can do little or nothing. Although we hope that some of the diseases which are now obstinate will yield to new discoveries, and will eventually be prevented altogether, there are always damaged people for whom new cures come too late. Our increased skill in saving the lives of people severely injured in car crashes, results in the survival of victims with brain damage, to restore whom is beyond our present resources. Many children born with physical or mental handicaps such as Spastics or Mongols, are likewise unlikely to be cured dramatically within our lifetime. Apart from clinical disease the defects which arise in old age leading to death are part of the natural decline of creatures who are mortal. All of us face intractable conditions in ourselves and in others.

Some of these conditions which we cannot cure we have tried to get rid of by institutionalisation. In the middle of the nineteenth century we developed a system to keep the mentally sick

* I find it necessary while discussing present attitudes to health, to accept the common assumption that wellness and illness depend upon the absence or presence of pathology. The assumption is later shown to be false. (p. 97).

4

in custody in remote and shunned mental hospitals. The stigma of mental illness has diminished in the last twenty years but is still common. For example the proposal to put a hostel for ex-prisoners or a half-way house for psychiatric patients in a respectable residential area still stirs up a hornet's nest. In Birmingham the mental hospital at Winson Green shares a common wall with the prison, and next to them is the site where the old fever hospital used to be. It is not just coincidence that many problem families are housed in the same area. It is as if the city had a vent through which it extruded its deviant members.

Because we cannot cure or solve the problem of mental sub-normality and old age we try to keep society free of trouble by a policy of 'putting away'.[4] We adopt the technique of sweeping society clean. We aim for a *sanitated society*, not a healthy society.

But most of all men try to hide death.

The current neurotic anxiety about such problems (organ transplants, and decisions about when to allow the old, the apparently permanently comatose and those with extensive brain injuries, to die) seems due to an inability to come to terms with the fear of death, with the result that quantity of life has become more important than quality. A man cannot become a mature person until he has reckoned with the test of his own dying, and in teaching the understanding of death the priest is at least as important as the doctor.[5]

Because they are associated with death, widows are social out-casts in Britain.[6] Many find strength and support in the com-panionship of other widows who form groups with the assistance of the Cruse Club.[7] For lack of this kind of acceptance many find themselves cast in the role of sick members of society to be treated by G.P.s or counselled for symptoms of unexpressed grief. Society cannot bear to share their grief and so we isolate and treat it. In this way, by 'approving' the concealment of feelings of grief and of carrying on as if nothing had happened we shape the situation into one of suppressed grief which takes the form of depression, anxiety or backache. In this way we mould bereavement into an illness which is socially acceptable. The experts such as doctors and consellors to whom society gives the responsibility of coping with such illness on its behalf, have a high status in society and a deep sense of fulfilment because they are wanted by society for its caring work.

Margaret Read has written about the influence of social attitudes and beliefs on health and illness. She describes the relationship between health and culture among the Navahos:

> The Navaho conception of health is very different from ours. For him, health is symptomatic of a correct relationship between man and his environment: his supernatural environment, the world around him, and his fellow man. Health is associated with good, blessing and beauty—all that is positively valued in life. Illness, on the other hand, bears evidence that one has fallen out of this delicate balance; it is usually ascribed to the breaking of one of the taboos which guide the behaviour of the Navahos, especially in the case of the conservative elders. . . . The Navaho does not make the distinction between religion and medicine that we do; for him they are aspects of the same thing. This is an important cultural fact that many workers in the health field have failed to realise; as a result, many doctors and nurses have antagonised their patients.[8]

The conception of health is related to a people's culture. For the Navahos health is associated with good, blessing and beauty. By contrast the Minister of Health in Great Britain in his annual report[9] is interested in diseases, handicap, death and ugliness. The Navaho conception of health is indeed very different from ours because they are a different people with different values. But it is very encouraging that many people in the West are now concerned about their environment and the conservation of wild creatures because they are beautiful.

Certain practical consequences follow from the way a society thinks about health. In particular its system of Health Care will reflect its ideas of health, as will its institutions (such as Hospitals and Health Centres), and the methods of practice of the professions deputed by a society to work for its 'health' (such as doctors and nurses). The National Health Service in Great Britain is still dominated by the concept of medicine based upon hospitals. Doctors and nurses are trained in hospitals and the influence of hospital consultants in the work of training is pre-eminent. Community doctors are not so highly regarded. A study of the interrelation between hospitals and the society which builds them can throw light on what society means by 'health' (see additional references, page 126).

HOSPITALS

It is men who make hospitals. As a picture tells us something about the artist who painted it, so a hospital tells us something about the men who make it. Down the centuries the hospital has served as hostel, prison, religious retreat and asylum: poor house, social assistance agency and school: waiting-room for death and therapeutic community. Men create an infirmary, a lazaretto, an asylum or a sanatorium as a response to some human affliction. The kind of response which men make to leprosy, mental subnormality, violence or drug dependence will be influenced by their current understanding of illness or deviant behaviour.

Our perception and understanding of what we see changes. Our perception and understanding of what we see differs from the perception and understanding of other men in other cultures and other ages. If a man fell down with an epileptic attack in the Middle East in the first century A.D. this behaviour would have been understood as due to possession by an evil spirit, and he would probably have been exorcised. In the Middle Ages he would probably have been bled. Although Hippocrates (400 B.C.) had first observed that epilepsy was caused by damage or disturbance of the brain, the belief in demonic possession still persisted in this country in the seventeenth century, when enemas, purges and fomentations were in vogue.[10] In the twentieth century the same behaviour would be understood in terms of an uncoordinated discharge of motor neurones and the patient would receive an injection of diazepam. It is likely that in another century our own understanding of epilepsy will seem as strange to our descendants, as our ancestors' ideas seem to us.

The types of hospital which we build, faithfully mirror our attitudes to life and death, illness and health: faithfully reveal in mud and wattle or bricks and concrete what man believes about himself, how he understands life, suffering and death; and how he responds to illness, whether by curing, caring, banishing or seeking to probe its causes.

For whether we consider a temple of Aesculapius, a medieval

7

hospice or a medical centre we are looking at a sensitive indicator of the style of life of the men who built it. 'Medical Centre' is the new name which accurately describes a concentration of technological services and resources for the diagnosis and treatment of disease. It is a typical expression of Western culture in the 1970s: one of the highest achievements of modern technology. But it is an institution dominated by medical interests. Power is in the hands of the doctors. The Medical Centre embodies medical values, in particular a dedicated research into the cause and nature of disease and its early diagnosis and treatment. It is a centre equipped to meet every kind of threat to life. The most costly treatment facilities are for deadly diseases in middle life such as coronary disease or cancer. An increasing number of patients are elderly.

It is men who make hospitals. What beliefs about illness lead us to build the kind of hospitals that we do? And what beliefs underlie the way we structure our Health Service?

THE HOSPITAL—A MIRROR OF SOCIAL BELIEFS ABOUT MAN IN SOCIETY

I have suggested that what people believe about illness shapes the nature of the hospital which they build. Money and staff will be devoted to the tasks which society believes to be the most important. The very site of the hospital may reflect social beliefs about certain illnesses. The psychiatric unit, removed from its suburban exile to the local District General Hospital, can be just as isolated on the topmost floor of the new building. And the mentally subnormal patients who are 'integrated' into the city in new hostels can be even more lonely than in their hospital ghetto.

It is possible to tease out the attitudes, beliefs and values upon which our system of hospital medicine and nursing is based, by thinking about the way hospitals are sited and built, by the way doctors and nurses, social workers and a large number of other professions do their work in hospital; by the way patients are admitted (or not admitted) and the priority accorded to certain types of treatment unit. Even salary scales are significant.

The things which are valued in hospital are not always openly stated. Assumptions are made about what is most important. This is not only true of hospitals but of other institu-

8

tions such as prisons. Whether the prison system is intended for rehabilitation of offenders into society or for their punishment and custody will influence the design of prisons, the recruitment and training of prison officers. If both beliefs exist together, as at present, there will be an uneasy truce between prison officers and welfare officers.

It is not easy to bring to consciousness for critical examination the assumptions upon which hospital medicine and nursing are based. Often assumptions are powerfully held because they are linked to the values, emotional fulfilment or prejudices of staff, patients and their families. Some of these assumptions may be expressed as follows:

(1) *The cure of disease is more important than the care of patients*

Modern technology is seen at its most successful in the service of mankind in a hospital. The doctor is a technical expert in diagnosis and treatment of disease. He expects to be, and is accepted as, the *de facto* leader of a team of professionals concerned with the restoration of patients. Of these professionals the nurse is primarily concerned with the basic bedside care of patients.

> When we talk of treatment (or cure) we do not often make it clear whether we mean the treatment of patients or the treatment of diseases. Yet there is a great deal of difference: to treat a disease means to attack, destroy or inhibit it in some way. To treat a patient, on the other hand, means to foster, nurture or care for his capacity for living. These are quite different kinds of activity.[11]

In the hospital there is a distinction (not a separation) made between these two activities. The salary scales of doctors and nurses (regardless of sex) declare in hard cash that skill in the cure of disease is more valued than skill in the care of patients. 'We can cure people these days without even knowing their names' is a surgeon's remark, and we can sense both the triumph and the arrogance in his words. In my study of the hospital[12] I pointed out how in this country today we are seeing a steady loss of the idea that caring for people is something of worth in itself, which does not have to be validated by clinical results. Psychiatric, geriatric and mentally subnormal hospitals which are predominantly concerned with the long-term care of patients, are the poorest among hospitals, in no way to be compared with the glamour of the new specialised surgical units which outgrow their modern buildings faster than they can be built. Such long-term care units are often staffed with nurses from overseas, from Africa, Mauritius and the Caribbean.

Cure is valued more highly than care. It would not be easy to argue for the allocation of a limited grant of money to the building of a sheltered workshop for a mentally handicapped hospital if medical opinion favoured a new renal transfusion unit for the Medical Centre. The latter can show an immediate return in terms of a few lives saved or prolonged: how can this be weighed against the intangible happiness, the lightening of boredom, or the sense of achievement in learning a skill (such a tiny skill perhaps) by hundreds of handicapped people in an overcrowded hospital? The same difficulty of evaluation is encountered in considering the relative merits of having babies at home or in hospital. The argument that really counts is the maternal and child mortality statistics. It is difficult to weigh other values, such as the relationship between parents and children, or family contentment, because they seem so imprecise when set against the risk of death. If you could prove that of the babies born at home, fewer committed suicide by the age of seventeen, people would take notice! But in other areas of life (adventure, exploration and sport) we run great risks for great rewards. Perhaps mountaineers' wives all have their babies at home!

R. L. Coser made a study in the U.S.A. of a hospital for old people which was divided into two units; one for rehabilitation and one for long-term care.

> In Catholic cultures taking care of suffering tends in itself to be considered a 'good deed', and nuns who engage in this activity are highly esteemed in the community. By contrast, in our achievement-orientated culture not much prestige is associated with the task *per se* of caring for patients. As a result if the hospital is defined as one that 'only' cares for patients who cannot get better, its abandonment of the culturally approved goal of 'curing the sick' has several significant consequences.[13]

Coser goes on to contrast the high morale of the rehabilitation unit with the low morale of the caring unit.

The nurse's role is changing from one who cares for the patient's morale and vitality, to one who assists the doctor in highly technical attacks upon disease. Nurses who have been trained in the role of assistant to a doctor, or as members of a team consisting of several different professions always led by a doctor, naturally feel frustrated if they find themselves as qualified nurses on a ward which caters mainly for long-stay patients who are of little clinical interest.

If there is a high expectation among patients and their families that disease will be cured, and this is what society values, then the nursing profession may attract nurses who find fulfilment in more medical and technical kinds of work. In fact most student nurses at present seem to come for training with a desire to care for people: but the system of training tends to crush it out of them. There is not necessarily a contradiction between curing disease and caring for patients, but an unbalanced training in clinical objectivity, and the discouragement of personal relationships between nurse and patient may result in a more impersonal style of nursing. I suspect that this is satisfying to some temperaments but not to others. It has been noted that nurses tend to withdraw from the ward when there is not much work to do, thus avoiding purely personal contacts with patients. Such relationship with patients as there is occurs when there are nursing procedures to be done.[14] Nurses who stand or sit and talk to patients are liable to be reprimanded and given other work to do. It is in caring for the elderly (geriatric nursing) that these attitudes and values are most sharply exposed. Old people need to be cared about, not just cared for; to be talked to, not talked at: and they have as much to give as receive from those who share their lives. This requires personal involvement as well as efficient nursing procedures.

In training staff for residential child care a different approach to care is adopted. It is recognised that staff require a gift for home-making. A study[15] of similar institutions for the care of handicapped children has shown marked differences in styles of care between nurses (hospital trained) and social workers (trained in residential care). Nurses, for example, did not eat with their children who consequently did not develop so readily the ability to feed themselves. Social workers paid more attention to the children's individual needs for privacy, companionship and personal clothing. In fact a residential child-care training seems to be more *human* than a nurse's training.

A similar approach is required in the care of long-stay patients who are handicapped mentally or physically.[16] This is not to say that rehabilitation, where possible, should be ignored, but simply to emphasise that in caring for people of all ages the support and maintenance of human dignity and personality is important. This, in itself, is worthwhile work. But in Western society it is not so esteemed, because we value the cure of disease and the deferment of death more highly.

It is possible that nursing will succumb to our present value system and become more and more technical: geriatric nursing will not then be fulfilling. Care for people without hope of recovery will have to be done by a different kind of nurse altogether: one who takes seriously the fact that non-nursing duties (and there are plenty of those in home-making) are often the way in which a nurse cares and gets to know her patients. But menial work in this country is increasingly being done by immigrants: is it they who will care for us in our old age, the underprivileged cared for by the underprivileged in mutual understanding?

Or nursing will recognise that its very *raison d'être* is threatened by a value system that is alien to its nature; namely the preference for the cure of disease to the care of people.

(2) *Staff assume power over patients*

Patients often feel that hospitals would still go on without them. Yet it is the presence of patients which makes possible the presence of staff as doctors, nurses, physiotherapists, social workers or administrators.

> More difficult are the problems of those who work in Institutions whose objectives are the relief of human suffering or the satisfaction of human aspirations. The problems they confront in performing their tasks are so akin to their own that it is frequently difficult, if not impossible, for them to distinguish clearly between their own needs and the needs of those they are trying to help.[17]

Staff need to be strong: perhaps this is one reason why doctors and other helping professions such as counsellors are attracted to the work. Staff are skilled, often in teams and working in their own professional institutions. The patient is unskilled, separated from his family in a strange place.

The very word 'patient'—the one who suffers—denotes one who is passive, who submits to the authority of skilled professionals who know what is best for him. Staff adopt a 'We'll take care of you' attitude which gives the patient and his relatives confidence. Not only then do patients regress as a part of the withdrawal from active life imposed by or expressed in illness, but the whole milieu of hospital life also favours regression. The patient is put to bed (sometimes unnecessarily), and deprived of his clothes. Encouraged by the strong attitudes of staff, he is reduced to dependence and compliance. The ideal patient is too often the one who conforms: the rebellious patient is troublesome[18] because he questions the whole basic assumption of dependency on which good behaviour is judged.

Few patients need to be treated as passive all the time. Most patients are responsible agents to some extent, even if only 10 per cent responsible. Many are 90 per cent or more capable of making choices and entering into partnership with staff in the work of making a good recovery. In conditions like alcoholism the acceptance of full responsibility by the person himself or herself may be the key to progress.

The assumption of power over patients can be very dehumanising for both parties—staff and patients. It is still possible to see a consultant with his retinue of doctors and ward sister, going round his 'beds' and discussing the case notes (laid ready on the foot of the bed) without speaking to the patient. Needless to say this does not happen with private patients, and 'personal attention'—at its very minimum the paying of attention to a person—is still advertised by private insurance firms as something which can be bought. The rich can buy respect. The poor get service.

There are some slow steady changes taking place in the relationship between patients and staff. They involve an adjustment of personal attitudes to one another. An authoritarian relationship between powerful staff and powerless patients is inappropriate in many clinical situations such as a Community Therapy Unit (see page 51). The discovery and recognition of an appropriate style of authority for a doctor to exercise is a mutual task for patients and staff.

The giving or withholding of information from patients and their families is a very complex human and ethical question. The assumption that if a patient is likely to die, then *he* is not told, but the family is told, is still a common clinical practice. I deliberately use the word clinical, because the withholding of information belongs to the pattern of behaviour which sees patients as *patients*—sometimes as individuals who can be isolated from their families. Staff share information[19] with patients when patients and their families are seen as *agents* with responsibility for making something out of their situation however tragic it might be. Sometimes we withhold information, openly to protect the patient but secretly to protect ourselves. We are afraid of the shock, the tears, the angry protest or hysteria. In hospital it is not easy to weather the storm with members of a family whom we hardly know. The general practitioner is far better placed for this kind of personal work with the family than hospital doctors. Illness, even terminal illness, is a slice of life to be lived. Because there is no hope of prolongation of life, that does not mean that the quality of the period left, long or short, cannot be rich in creative work, or loving relationships. Ignorance of his true situation may neuter a patient, and may deprive a husband and wife of a great opportunity to make something out of their crisis together. It may also make the subsequent bereavement sharper.

(3) *Individuals are separate from one another*

In hospital more attention is paid to the individual in his/her separateness than to a person in his/her relatedness to family and society.

Every individual is unique, but our uniqueness is developed through interdependence and interaction with other unique individuals.

'A man is a man by reason of other men'

(Xhosa saying)

'There is no such thing as being a separate person'

(Hephzibah Menuhin)

'There is no person without encounter with other persons'

(Paul Tillich)

14

Full human development cannot take place as if an individual is the only pebble on the beach. The uniqueness of man sets him free 'to do his own thing', but only if doing his own thing does not limit the ability of other men to do their own thing also. It is part of the tragedy of the world as we know it that even such an elementary thing as full physical development is only possible for a minority of people. In the United Kingdom most children have grown taller than their parent's generation because since 1945 they have received an adequate diet—but only by the exploitation of Africa and other countries where food is short and children do not reach their full height. When we go on to consider the underdeveloped abilities for creative work and life among some of the peoples of Africa or the oppressed peasants of South America, the luxury of the Western way of life, so full of opportunities for individual growth and development, must be seen as bought at the price of other people's health. At cost to whom am I healthy?

Doctors in hospital deliberately focus on the individual patient. It has been part of the strength of hospital medicine for doctors to be able to isolate the patient, diagnose his disease and concentrate detailed research and therapeutic power upon a localised lesion or bodily system. Important discoveries have been made through specialism in Medicine and Surgery. The necessary objectivity has been balanced by a long humanist tradition among doctors. Detachment from a patient (in order to observe him and make a diagnosis) has been counterbalanced by a warm patient/doctor relationship. The old family doctor practised a style of medicine with a blend of skill and humanity.

Today these values are being eroded. Families are now regarded as a source of information for the staff and as an amenity for the patient, rather than as organically involved in the health/sickness situation with the patient. Families are extraneous to the work of the hospital: they feel powerless. Doctors are fully capable of curing the individual without his relatives. In the creative process of recovery relatives are spectators, receivers of good news or bad news, until the day of discharge when quite suddenly the patient is theirs again. Speck[20] has emphasised the importance of enlisting the active help of relatives on a ward in caring for patients. But for this to be successful the nursing staff must gain insight into the difficulties which relatives have, and be willing to offer the support and understanding which they require. Speck describes the difficulties of the hospital visitor as concerned principally with communication, fear and feelings of inadequacy.

In a seminar with staff nurses in a large teaching hospital, the subject which they put forward for discussion was the fact that their present House Officers (junior doctors) were very bad at coming to see the relatives when requested to do so. Several staff nurses had had experience of phoning the doctors up and being met with a refusal to come. This was discussed as a failure in communication. After further thought, however, it was seen to be an example of very clear communication. There are few better ways of telling a patient's relatives exactly what you think of them than to refuse to see them. Silence is a very powerful communication.

Many children's hospitals, but by no means all, now make arrangements for mothers to be admitted with their small children. The research work of Bowlby[21] and others [22] has shown the disastrous effects of the separation of small children from their mothers where no adequate substitute mothering is provided. A situation which arose in a children's ward illustrates very well the different way in which hospital staff may perceive people.[23] A mother took her baby to hospital with a broken leg. With some difficulty she persuaded the ward staff to let her come into hospital with him. When the ward sister returned from holiday she did her best to persuade the mother to leave the baby and go home. 'After all,' she said, 'he's not very ill.' 'It's not a matter of how *ill* he is,' replied his mother, 'it's a matter of how *old* he is. I'm the only person he trusts, and if I leave him alone among strangers and in pain, with his leg immobilised in plaster, he will feel completely betrayed.'

The ward sister was thinking of the child in the hospital frame of reference, that is in the narrow terms of his sickness. The mother was thinking of the child in a personal frame of reference, identifying herself with the child's feelings and needs. The one woman saw the child as a separable individual: the other as integrally belonging to her—inseparable without trauma. The two women were looking on the child in completely different ways. The effect of a professional training actually affects our perceptions, we *see* things, people and events differently. All too little attention is given to this in professional training, although the work of Abercrombie[24] with medical students shows its importance. In particular, when we focus upon what is wrong with people our vision tends to become narrowed.

Not only does a patient belong to his family, he is also a member of the community. Too long we have concentrated on the cure of sick individuals without paying sufficient attention to the social conditions which often give rise to illness. How can you treat patients in hospital with chronic bronchitis and resultant heart failure without also paying attention to the control of the industrial smoke which they are breathing? Smokeless zones in Britain's cities are a comparatively recent measure towards improvement. Individuals are still being treated in psychiatric hospitals without sufficient attention being given to the family, social or work situation which has stressed the patient.

The full folly of individualism can be seen most clearly where we have exported our hospital tradition overseas. In my own hospital in Ghana three of the main clinical problems which helped to fill the out-patient department every day were: Malnutrition, Venereal Disease and Tuberculosis; conditions which often stemmed from the system of migrant labour which exists in many parts of Africa. Labourers from the Northern Territories came a thousand miles to the South to pick up casual work. They lived in overcrowded conditions in a tribal ghetto of the town, ate food to which they were not used, and, separated from their wives and families, slept with local women or prostitutes. In hospital we saw it as our task to treat the casualties of a labour system against the injustice of which few medical voices were raised. For we were trained as doctors to find our fulfilment in the clinical treatment of individuals—and it *is* very fulfilling work indeed. But we have often been blind to the social dimensions of disease.

Poverty is still the major cause of disease in the world. It used to be said that the doctor was the natural advocate of the poor. When Doctor Christian Barnard visited South America, they filled a football stadium in Brazil twice over to acclaim his achievement in making the first heart transplant. Yet the tens of thousands of peasants in his audience could not afford the necessary pennies to buy simple medicine to rid their own intestines of worms.[25] In another part of *the same country* where Barnard's heart transplant was achieved Oxfam was supplying measles vaccine for malnourished children. This produces in me

17

the same kind of reaction that the atom bomb must have produced in a physicist. For now we are becoming giants in medical technology but dwarfs in its responsible use.

Of course preventive medicine has taken account of social factors. Medical Officers of Health however are less highly regarded than hospital doctors although they certainly make a greater contribution to social well-being. I was in Ghana when the millionth citizen received his anti-polio injection, and there were newspaper headlines about it. Here again so much work is aimed at the prevention of disease in individuals—millions of them perhaps. But the greatest cause of disease in the world— poverty—has roots in the whole style of a people's life. A policy of saving individual lives may lead people into other difficulties such as hunger and unemployment unless medicine is seen as one facet of the development of that people's corporate life together. It is this innate individualism of doctors and our system of medicine in the West which is making the transition from hospital medicine to community medicine so difficult (see page 22).

Where attention is being paid to the development of the quality of life which men and women build together, there a different kind of medicine is beginning to make its appearance. The idea of the corporateness of man is bound to change Western medicine which is at present so individualistic in its outlook. There are already hospitals—so very few—where families can be admitted together, e.g. the Cassel Hospital,[26] because it is recognised that a great deal of illness has no respect for skin as that which defines where a man begins and where he ends. A sick man, a sick family, a sick society: all three are interrelated.

(4) *The provision of health is a task for experts*

The advantages of specialism in hospital medicine are evident. A specialist is able to concentrate on a limited area of pathology (e.g. diseases of the eye), to develop a particular gift (e.g. the still largely 'intuitive' gift of diagnosis), to acquire knowledge in a difficult area (e.g. blood chemistry), to develop a particular skill (e.g. bone surgery) or to pursue research focused on a particular problem (e.g. the electron microscopic study of abnormal muscle fibres).

The disadvantages of specialism are by no means always as readily admitted. We are a society which rewards specialists with the highest honours and salaries in medicine. We give less status to a generalist such as a general medical practitioner, and even suggest—a complete contradiction in terms—that we should have specialists in general practice as if we could in some way give him status by using the tag 'specialist'.

The multiplication of specialists, each developing their own language, journals and Royal Colleges, results in a problem of communication. The presence or absence of communication between different professions can seriously promote or hinder the well-being of both staff and patients in a hospital—or in society as a whole.

Every time we increase our ability to discover defects in human biology and behaviour the complexity of disease grows. A system of medicine based upon knowledge of disease cannot produce health. It can only discover more disease and create the very needs which it is supposed to meet. A Hospital Service can never be brought up to a desirable standard in terms of resources and staff.[27] The Social Services are in the same difficulty because even elementary surveys in city slums (e.g. the compilation of a list of 'children at risk') reveal human needs far beyond the resources of the existing services.

Lambourne has shown[28] that our present ways of trying to obtain health are in fact too specialised. This results in tunnel vision: that is, we have developed a highly focused skill to solve immediate and local crises. The surgeon is a good example, he can actually identify the part at fault and may be able to remove or repair it. But our very skill with detail renders us blind to the wider context; we suffer from loss of vision of the whole—the whole person, the whole family, the whole community, the whole environment. A simplified version of Lambourne's map is reproduced[29] with his own warning:

> The concepts map is very tentatively offered to help . . ., not as a determinant of thought but as a stimulus to reflection. It is hoped it will be taken seriously but not too seriously!!

The diagram illustrates how in our British system of health care we have become over-specialised in medical concepts related to the eradication of diseases understood as pathological

A Concepts Map of the Practice of Medicine
(* Shows concentration of effective concepts used in medical education)

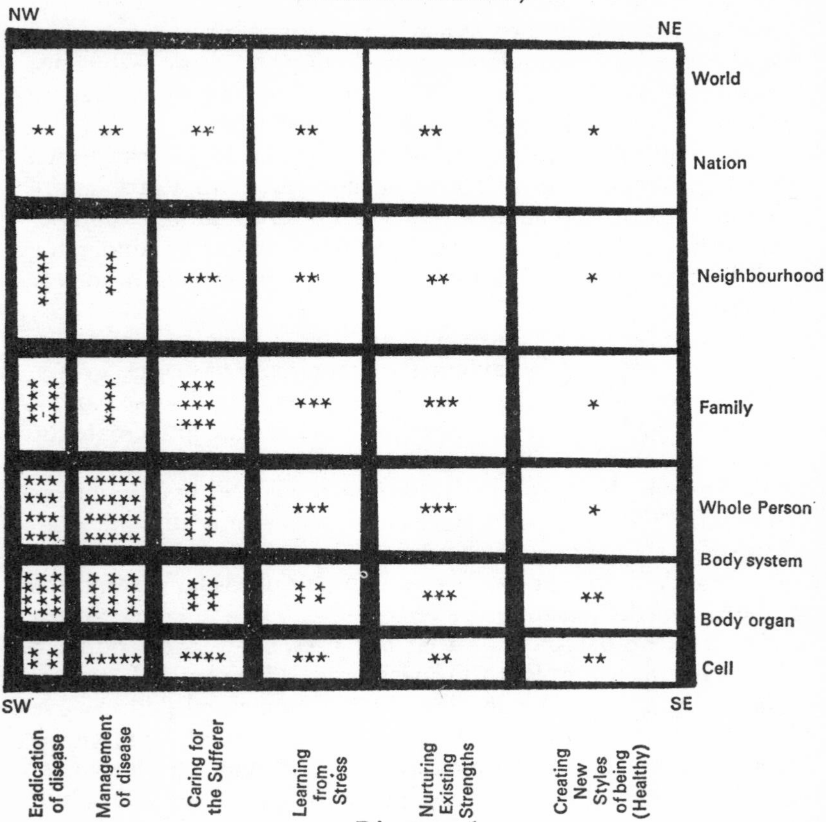

Diagram 1

The vertical North–South dimension indicates a *hierarchy of contexts* (each level providing a context for the level below it) within which a particular type of caring, curing or health-enhancing person (e.g. doctor, nurse, teacher, minister of religion or mother) operates. From South to North the context enlarges from *cell* to *organ and systems of the body*, to *whole* person, to *family*, to *neighbourhood*, to *nation*, to *world*. Examples of doctors operating predominantly in these different contexts are, moving Northwards: the molecular biologist, the specialist surgeon, the psychosomatic physician, the general practitioner, the medical officer of health, the ecologist in a team advising a developing nation, and a medical philosopher envisaging a cosmic Utopia.

The horizontal West–East dimension is concerned with those *different concepts of what healing is*, each of which can dominate a particular professional identity and shape the ideology of medicine which evolves around it. Successively from West to East are *eradication of disease isolated from its context, management of disease in its proper context, care of sufferer, learning from stress, nurturing existing strengths* and *creating new ways of being healthy*.

20

conditions which can be localised. The skills, temperaments or gifts which are related to wider vision and longer term planning are far too thinly represented. The map does not pass judgement on the relative values of different skills, but points to the lack of balance in Western ideas about health care. This lack of balance may well be due to the value which society places upon immediate solutions to crises. Possible causes of this are discussed below (page 25).

There is a striking similarity between Lambourne's concepts map and the first diagram in *The Limits to Growth*.[30] The Club of Rome's diagram entitled 'Human Perspectives' illustrates how far the majority of human concerns are those which affect only family or friends over a short period of time. Very few people have a global perspective that extends far into the future.

The comparison between these two diagrams underlines the over-specialisation of Western health care. We excel at coping with a particular crisis such as acute appendicitis. We plan a hospital service based upon community needs where 'community' means 'population'; that is the sum of individuals living in a given area. But the members of a community are more like the members of a body than marbles in a box. Community health, which involves an appreciation of the life and morale of groups as a whole and their aspirations for the good life, eludes too specialised a scrutiny.

There are other repercussions in society due to specialisation. Over two hundred hospitals (in Britain in 1974) have full-time organisers of voluntary services. There are also many voluntary societies concerned for people in different kinds of trouble—such as the Samaritans (suicide) and the Richmond Fellowship (emotionally ill people). Volunteers are selected and receive different amounts of training: this is essential for work like that done by Marriage Guidance Counsellors. But the word 'amateur' is in danger of becoming a pejorative term, synonymous with someone who doesn't really know his job. Today you almost have to take a training course before you can visit your grandmother!

At the beginning of the National Health Service it was Nye Bevan who said:

'There is no substitute for the good neighbour.'

But today, if my neighbour is depressed, then that need not interfere with my weekend arrangements: after all that is what the Samaritans are for. (This is not to disparage an excellent organisation; simply to emphasise how we may misuse it.) By too much respect for the 'expert' we can be robbed of the simple ways by which we express our mutual care for one another. The care of neighbour for neighbour is the cement of local community (see page 50).

The doctor trained in the hospital tradition of the Western world is now often found to be too specialised for the kind of health care systems required in the third world.* It has taken some years for African doctors, trained in a Western style of medicine, to discover the true medical needs of their own people and to make an appropriate response to them. At first when a British colony like the Gold Coast became an independent African country—Ghana—the medical service was Western in philosophy, training and structure, though the doctors were mostly African. The first concern was with standards, and a flow of African students continued to come to the medical schools of the West. Doctors returned to the colonial hospitals in African towns and cities, rather than to the rural areas where most of the population lives. Where else could they give expression to the introjected beliefs about medicine and surgery which they had learnt in European hospitals? Where else find the special equipment upon which they were so skilfully trained to be dependent? But they were too specialised for the needs of Africa. Professional standards had become an idol.

Bryant[31] summed up the resulting problem in this way:

Large numbers of the world's people, perhaps more than half, have no access to health care at all, and for many of the rest the care they receive does not answer the problems they have.

And Morley[32] in Nigeria thus:

Three-quarters of our population are rural, yet three-quarters of our medical resources are spent in the towns

* The terms used to describe some nations as 'poor' or 'underdeveloped' are not satisfactory. The phrase 'Third World' is used as the least patronising term in common usage. We are really One World.

where three-quarters of our doctors live; three-quarters of the people die from diseases which could be prevented at low cost, and yet three-quarters of medical budgets are spent on curative services.

King[33] shows what sharp differences of opinion have developed within the medical profession itself about how to practise medicine, about our professional identity. Doctors being trained today in the hospital style of medicine may be faced with a personal crisis.

Lambourne[34] writes:

> I was recently in a city in the Philippines and met a young Christian doctor who said he was going to be a neuro-surgeon. His boss, whom he very properly admired, is a neuro-surgeon and he very naturally wants to be not only like his boss, but be better. That's quite understandable for the young man, but it is tragic because he is now fixed on a course of being excellent as a Christian and a doctor which is not relevant to his original chosen task which was to cure people. He will go to America, because that's where the most excellent neuro-surgeons work, for his further training, and this will make it impossible for him to work anywhere in the Philippines but in Manila, and perhaps not even there. If by any chance he later hears a call from God to go and work in the rural districts, he will have to fight his professional identity, his built-in concept of excellent doctoring, for the rest of his life.

A doctor may have too narrow a perception of the life of the people as a whole, because of his specialism in the prevention and cure of disease. But if a doctor does not respond to the real situation of human need by an appropriate style of being a doctor, he becomes, possibly unwittingly, an agent of oppression. In Africa a large number of migrant labourers attend hospital out-patients with diseases which are due to their living and working conditions. As a doctor in hospital I treated individual sick labourers, thus easing the symptoms of a cheap labour policy. But for doctors to be silent in the face of an injustice of whose consequences in terms of disease they are well aware, is to be party to the injustice.

Medicine is one of the widest information services which a

society has about the symptoms of poverty and stress in the life of its people. Thousands of patients in the territories of Africa which used to be governed by Britain, were treated in mission and government hospitals for diseases such as leprosy, bilharzia, Guinea Worm and malnutrition as if treatment was a worthwhile service to individuals on their own often *without at the same time* taking effective political and religious initiatives to tackle the poverty of which such diseases are symptoms. Doctors often try to practice medicine as if their art could be separated from its political context.

This narrowness of perception tinges the subject of medical ethics with unreality. Medical ethics cannot be discussed within a medical ghetto as if medicine was not a service belonging to society as a whole.

Our whole present medical understanding and Christian understanding requires that we spend great sums for the treatment of one person, whereas if we could re-apply the expenditure you could save many lives. The real, the new, the excellent men of tomorrow, will at a certain point be required to say 'No, this cannot be done', and 'This particular person has to be sacrificed'. This makes clear what has always been true but often denied, namely, that the practice of medicine is an ethico-political art. What we have been discussing today reminds us that many of the major ethical decisions confronting the Christian doctor are not those involved in the choice between different acts towards the one patient in front of us, such as when to pull out the intravenous tube or stop artificial respiration, but a kind of political decision involved in health care planning which decides quite literally whether thousands of people would live or die.[35]

King[36] has shown that the catchment area of a hospital in East Africa is mostly limited to those who live within two or three miles of its doors. Therefore to decide to build a hospital in one place and not in another spells life for some and death for others. To decide to spend money on training a neurosurgeon to save a few people from dying of brain tumours, means that the same money is unavailable to save a thousand people from the same area dying from other diseases. The siting of hospitals and the expenditure of money on one

24

kind of resource and not another is an ethico/medical/political decision.

Doctors, Western trained, must accept responsibility for the public understanding of their art which has resulted in the kind of medical services described above (page 22), so that 'Large numbers of the world's people, perhaps more than half, have no access to health care at all', and 'three quarters of our population are rural, yet three quarters of our medical resources are spent in the towns . . .'.

These world-wide effects of specialism and tunnel vision in Western medicine must lead us to question whether this style of being a doctor is in fact the most suitable in Western society itself. We have emphasised the importance of sensitivity to the whole life of a people. Awareness of this wider context is a necessary basis for a system of Medicine which is to subserve a people's social aspirations for health. Health is a public creation not a private specialism. The general practitioner is closer to the daily lives of his patients than the consultant. It is time we began to plan a system of medical/social training directed to general practice, with a spin off into hospital consultancy, rather than a system which trains hospital doctors with a spin off into general practice. The new medical school at Southampton,[37] the chair in Community Health at Nottingham, and the development of training in family medicine in Birmingham and London may be steps in the right direction.

(5) *Every problem has a solution**

One of the methods of technology is to identify a particular problem and to solve it. Doctors have made great use of this method, and medical research in the last twenty-five years has solved some of the major causes of human suffering. Examples are the discovery of a drug to cure leprosy, an insecticide to kill the Anopheles mosquito (carrier of malaria) and antibiotics with power to prevent the multiplication of a wide range of organisms causing such conditions as pneumonia, bone abscesses, yaws and tuberculosis.

In order to solve a problem it is necessary to collect

* I am using the form 'Problem/Solution' because it is in common use among doctors and social workers. But problems cannot be fully stated nor clear solutions implied. Human situations are complex. Although our knowledge is always incomplete, partial knowledge is real knowledge.

information and develop techniques, often of a highly specialised nature, and focus them upon a particular situation. An excellent example of highly focused research was the discovery of the exoerythrocytic cycle of the malaria parasite by Short and Garnham.[38]

In hospital a focused approach is highly appropriate in surgery and radiotherapy as well as in research. But what is appropriate in one situation·may be inappropriate in another. Because it is so effective to narrow the context in surgery and research, we tend to use the method too generally, and misapply it in human situations where it may be essential to see a patient (such as an alcoholic) in his family and social context.

Our present approach to abortion in Britain is an example. An unwanted pregnancy is now often spoken of as if a foetus was something that had gone wrong: it is an unwanted growth, alien to its host like a cancer, and therefore a problem to be solved by removal in the same way. The problem may be presented to the obstetrician as an ethical choice between operating on the body of a woman or not. The doctor may be well aware of the human stresses related to keeping the baby, of the social dimensions of the problem, that a man is also involved (it is part of his body tissue, this growth, as well as hers) and families on both sides, and more generally the attitudes and values of the society of which the doctor himself is a member. It is a human situation as well as an ethical, social, political and clinical problem. But doctors are regarded by society as problem-solvers. To whom should we more naturally turn for the removal of an unwanted growth than a doctor? Doctors have become the victims of their own professional style.

Euthanasia is beginning to present itself in exactly the same way. Doctors now feel it necessary to defend their professional identity as those who save life rather than take it. But I doubt if this is the crucial area for debate. The discussion of euthanasia arises in Western society because of its attitudes to old age and death, its lavish use of resources to prolong life, and its poor standards of clinical and nursing care of the dying (with the outstanding exception of some special units or hospices).[39] It is in the area of changing social values that debate is required.

A second area in which the problem-solving approach is

shaping human behaviour is in the use of tranquillisers and sedatives. The circumstances in which these pills are now used are often normal situations of distress. I use the word 'normal' with hesitation because stress is now so widely regarded as an evil—just a problem to be solved—rather than as a possible source of good.

When there was a strike of local government employees in Britain, gravediggers did not work, and there was a delay in funeral arrangements. A funeral director, interviewed on the television news, commented that many families were in distress, and were having to call general practitioners to help them with a prescription for tranquillisers.

At a meeting of general practitioners in the Midlands the question was asked: 'If a patient who has recently been bereaved gets depressed would you prescribe a drug to control the depression?' The doctors present were equally divided between those who would prescribe as a matter of course: and those who would not. When a psychiatrist asked: 'And if your patient was depressed, how long would you let the depression last before you prescribed?' he was answered 'One week'. Whereupon another doctor present commented: 'I hope you'd let me be depressed for longer than a week if I lost my wife!'

It is hypocritical that the adult world should condemn the very few young people who are dependent on drugs such as LSD and heroin, when so many adults are themselves dependent on drugs such as barbiturates and tranquillisers for their own stability. Pain, stress, discomfort of any kind, have become problems to be solved. What is and what is not acceptable is to a large extent socially determined. Doctors as public educators are among the important determiners of social opinion about what is acceptable and what is not. The ready prescription of pills to solve personal problems gives a medical blessing to the popular perception of stress as bad. The long-term social effects of this are likely to be serious (see page 74).

Social workers are also expected to solve problems. Much of their work is concerned with personal and family crises, some of which can be solved, but many of which must be borne. Social workers themselves are far more aware than the hospital professions, of the personal, family and social dimensions of illness, of the ignorance and apathy of ordinary people, of poverty, bad housing and poor environment as causes of frustration, illness and breakdown; of the sickness of society which finds its expression in individuals and families partly predisposed by temperament or circumstance. In social work we speak (significantly) of a 'case load'.

Very few members of the Health and Social Service professions visit people at home when they are well. Health Visitors do so, for no other reason than that there is a small child in the house. However, Health Visitors are now tending to work more with doctors, and this will surely lead to more home visiting to see people who are in some kind of trouble.[40] I know of one general practitioner (but only one, so I imagine it is unusual) who visits the family when they first join his list. He believes it is important to meet them for the first occasion when they are well and do not need him: this is particularly true of children. A clergyman can visit people in their homes purely because they live in his geographical area, but he too tends to visit them nowadays at times of crisis when people are ill, bereaved, or have just moved house. The more efficiently we look for problems the more we find, and the more problem-solvers we need. We behave as if what is wrong with a man is more important than what is right: but this is a perversion of human relationships, even for a clinician. A concern for what is wrong and bad and evil tends to narrow vision: whereas to pay attention to what is good widens our vision.

Is it a coincidence that in Britain the rapid development of caring professions coincides with the loss of colonial territories overseas? Are we a nation with a predominant streak in our make-up for domination, for patronisation, and so for care?

Is it a coincidence that in Britain the rapid development of caring professions coincides with a period of dramatic diminishment in church attendance and religious commitment? Why do problems fascinate us? What is it that we fear in ourselves and care for in others so assiduously? Is it the things which remind us of mortality?

(6) *Death is the worst thing that can happen to a man*

Many social attitudes and much behaviour in hospital can only be explained on the assumption that 'death is the worst thing that can happen to a man.' We note a reluctance to speak about death or to tell patients about a fatal prognosis, the withdrawal of attention from patients for whom doctors can do no more, pointless resuscitation and prolongation of life, the allocation of funds and staff to Intensive Treatment Units and the impoverishment of hospitals primarily concerned with care, all this behaviour is rooted in our present social 'taboo' of death. We are a death-fearing society, and the practice of medicine and nursing is influenced by such social fears and expectations. Our understanding of 'health' in Western culture is also captive to the fear of death. Our 'Health' service is concerned for the prevention and cure of illness—of every reminder of death. The status and power of the doctor in hospital derives from his skill, real and imaginary, to prevent death. Surveys of the work of hospital chaplains and of the expectations which patients and staff have of their work, show that they are widely associated with the idea of death.[41] Staff see a useful role for the chaplain more clearly in terminal illness and death than in any other situation.

We defer consideration of death to the end of life because we do not accept it as a part of what being human means. But the hospital is a place of truth where the facts of mortality must be faced. Although every medical student learns 'Thou shalt not strive, officiously to keep alive', yet doctors find it difficult to let patients die. Hospital staff are at the receiving end of a social fear of death, and feel death as a failure. If you do not strive officiously to keep alive you may come under criticism from relatives, and even incur litigation. Such are the group dynamics that ward staff will attempt to deceive patients, and a doctor will resuscitate elderly and clinically unsuitable patients to the point where one must ask 'Whose needs are being met? Patient's, family's or doctor's?' Misplaced clinical enthusiasm which will not let a patient die in peace, suggests an underlying anxiety about death. It is often younger doctors who do this; some are themselves conscious of the pressures to act in this way.[42] Student nurses commonly raise this question in open discussions. Nurses, in fact, are usually far more balanced than doctors about death: they are more often with the patient, it is to their care that the doctor leaves the patient when he can do no more, and it is nurses who lay out the body. They have a natural instinct about death which is rooted in their understanding of birth.

I have described elsewhere[43] an illustrative case of the

29

conspiracy of silence which may develop in a hospital ward. People who work in hospital quite apart from their own feelings about death, are at the receiving end of the feelings of a society which asks them to avert and conceal death. Hospital staff represent our social values in their behaviour. They express the attitudes of society, and reaffirm them.

Death throws its shadow forward: we know today that we shall die one day. In Western culture there is an unhealthy denial of that reality. It is not an open reaction with an 'Eat, drink and be merry, for tomorrow we die'. It is a secret denial because we fear that death is the worst thing that can happen to a man. Therefore we pretend we can hide mortality and such whispers of mortality as sickness until the end. We have put death into a ghetto. So we have created for ourselves the problem of terminal illness, and the closely related problem of old age.

The entitlement of a conference of the Institute of Religion and Medicine—'The Waiting Room for Death'—highlights a concern among clergy, doctors, nurses and social workers for a whole constellation of pastoral problems which are multiplying around the death event: the care of the dying; How do we define death?; How to communicate a bad prognosis; Who should tell whom what?; Grief and mourning. Shall we live to see the establishment of a specialty in grief and mourning?[44]

In a society where death is denied, old age is also denied. There is in all the cells of our bodies a biological process of breakdown, which slowly gains ascendancy over the rebuilding processes of life. Biological death may be regarded therefore as a process, not merely an event. The menopause, loss of energy, failing memory, these are foreshadowings of death, and those who become old find that they also share in our social denial of death.

Up to the age of seventy-five many elderly people are still active and lively minded. Others age earlier. But after retirement, when we stop paid employment, we quickly lose contact with old colleagues and workmates. What then is our role? What then is our value? Few people with experience in the care of old people would disagree with the statement that one of the most important factors in the maintenance of health at all ages is a sense of personal worth, of being wanted. A sense of one's own identity. There is no group of people in greater confusion about their identity or civic worth than the elderly, for they approach with uncertain steps the mystery of death which is the ultimate threat to our self and to our meaning.

The elderly receive a Christmas bonus, charity and free bus passes, because they are poor: but not an adequate income as of right because they are human—whether man or woman, married or single, sick or healthy, working or not.

For the working class, who age earlier, loss of meaning is no novel experience to be encountered first in old age; they have been deprived of their meaning long before.[45] If there is a loss of sense of purpose in life throughout society, then this sense of meaninglessness will be sharpest in old age, and we shall not be able to restore a sense of human dignity to one age group alone. Young people are affected by this vision of the future: they see what lies ahead of them and feel devalued in the present.

We may devalue old people, tolerate their poverty and write books on their loneliness, but they have a place in society. It is society which must not rob them of their place. At present we structure their role as 'in need of care' and we may depute hospital staff to care for them on our behalf. There is a risk that we shall find it increasingly convenient, as with birth and death, to make provision for that care in institutions.

In the West we try to reach health by the eradication of such defects as can be cured, by the solution of such problems as may be solved, and by a denial of the incurable and insoluble—by their exclusion into institutions. We aim to have a sanitated society swept clean of such badness. Death, the great insoluble incurable fact, is denied. This denial of death is the root cause of our denials of its foreshadowings. Death is believed to be dominant over life. We really do believe in death: talk of resurrection and a future life is thought to be fantasy. Sartre vividly describes in his novels the resultant meaninglessness which has spread through life. Medicine cannot but share in this loss of meaning, for the style of being a doctor is influenced by the society and culture of the day. The health machine has begun to falter. Prolongation of life is not necessarily good in itself: it is a possibility for good or evil. There is more to being human than just being well. It is not the doctor's fault if his

31

powerful skills to prolong biological life bring greater problems to humanity in terms of quality of life; if the man or woman whose life he has saved lives on into an old age of poverty and a sense of worthlessness. It could be better to die young, alive: than to live old, dead.

What's so bad about death?
death is part of living
wholeness includes a healthy attitude tow. death.
why are we afraid of death
its part of being human

PART II

The Growth of New Ideas

PUBLIC HEALTH

In Part I we have described how our understanding of health shapes our Health Care Service. We have teased out some of the attitudes and assumptions which underlie a medical system based on hospitals. Our beliefs about health become recognisable in the professional style of doctors, nurses and social workers, in the concepts which dominate their training, and in the shape of the buildings which they design for their tasks. In fact beliefs have very expensive implications.

We now recognise that every system of medicine and of medical care has implicit within it a philosophy of personal and political behaviour.[46]

We can see, for example, how Public Health has slowly influenced ideas in medicine over the past fifty years. Lambourne writes:

Thirty years ago Public Health was a small special subject in the medical curriculum, a speciality among others, and having little influence on the main thinking and practice of medical care.

Fifteen years ago Public Health approaches were to be found within each specialty but without this changing the specialties' central concepts and practices. Epidemiology still primarily referred to traditional epidemic diseases of an infectious or contagious nature.

Now concepts and methods formerly peculiar to public health have become so central to medicine that they change the dominant concepts of health and medical care. As a result, for example, the success of a medical procedure is no longer measured by the summation of its effect on the same pathology in a number of individuals. Instead it is measured by considering its effects on a whole number of factors previously considered to be the interest solely of other specialties as diverse as agriculture, education, political philosophy, transportation and industry.[47]

In 1948 when Britain created a National Health Service political concepts, previously implicit in medicine, became explicit. Not that medicine was non-political before 1948, but in the new Health Service medicine became what it potentially was—a service to which all citizens have an equal right, and for which all citizens have a political responsibility. The distribution of resources for wellness became in principle a matter of justice instead of wealth within this country, although internationally it remains a matter of wealth.

In the field of Public Health, for example, doctors are concerned with the purity and adequacy of water supplies, so their attention must be given to reservoirs and all the priorities related to conservation of the environment. Public Health doctors are also concerned about the quality of food we eat, so their attention must be given to food preparation and to agricultural and dairy policies at home, as well as imported foods from overseas. These two issues alone involve wide political decisions affecting our own nation and others.

Health educators cross the frontiers of many disciplines and government departments. Health visitors are able to visit our homes to give instruction; midwives are trained educators and naturally teach expectant mothers in ante-natal clinics; teachers in schools give sex instruction to their pupils with great possibilities for enhancing or damaging interpersonal and family health; and mothers create health or illness in their children by the information, attitudes and life-styles to which they introduce their children.

Public Health doctors have, therefore, widened our concepts of health in ways which we might represent in a diagram:[48]

34

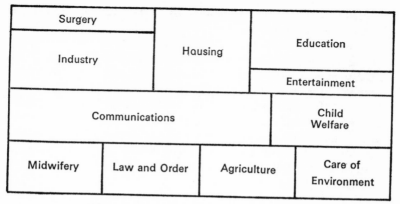

Diagram 2. Some Components of Health

The question of priorities to be given to each component raises matters of political choice: political because health concerns the quality of our life together, in a family, a neighbourhood, a nation and internationally; a choice because our resources are limited.

Health involves choice: health is a value word. The choice facing a regional committee as to whether to devote resources to new kidney machines or to an adventure playground in a deprived area is a sharp ethical decision, and the criteria of evaluation are difficult. In the city of Birmingham there is a long waiting-list for hospital admission, but the city has a very fine system of ring roads and tunnels of which we are justly proud: a choice has been made. How much money should go to education, how much to curing illness? A fine new Medical Centre must be built at the expense, perhaps, of improvements to old school buildings in the inner ring of the city. The endeavour to build a healthy society is an ethico-political art. Some ways will now be described in which these ideas are enlarging our understanding of health, and changing our styles of medical and nursing practice.

COMMUNITY DEVELOPMENT

In Part I we suggested that the kind of hospital medicine developed in the West does not meet the needs of the people in the third world. The situation was summed up in two quotations (page 22) which indicated:

(1) that perhaps half the world's people have no access to health care at all, and for many of the rest the care they received does not answer the problems which they have.
(2) that there are countries where three-quarters of the population are rural, but three-quarters of the medical resources are spent in the towns, where three-quarters of the doctors are: and that three-quarters of the people die from diseases preventable at low cost, yet three-quarters of medical budgets are spent on curative services.

Hospital medicine, based upon towns, still persists as the basic model for a medical service. For example:[49]

The capital involved in the construction of the new hospital in Lusaka, Zambia (£5,000,000), would have been enough to finance the construction of 250 health centres which, if each served 20,000 people could cover the entire population.

The capital costs of a single teaching hospital in Africa may exceed the entire annual recurrent health budget of the country in which it is situated.[50] The Office of Health Economics[51] presents facts and figures which make it seem inevitable that for financial reasons alone, if for no others, preventive medicine will become a priority above curative services.

Much is already being done. Mass vaccination to control smallpox (e.g. in Ethiopia), malaria eradication campaigns (e.g. in Sri Lanka) and the work of the World Health Organisation in many directions (e.g. the prevention of poliomyelitis in Ghana) are examples of what is being done. But often these are special campaigns superimposed upon a system of hospital medicine. The same assumptions underlie both hospital and preventive medicine. An emphasis on the latter in tropical countries is economic common sense and makes possible a fairer distribution of scarce resources. But both are concerned with disease. Both provide wellness.

Because there is so much illness in the third world and the types of illness (for example due to parasites) are so grossly debilitating, doctors who give priority to preventive medicine are able to convey possibilities for a new quality of life beyond simple wellness. Medicine becomes the vehicle, as it were, of qualities of life greater than those it brings itself. It is only when an anti-malarial scheme sets a population free from parasites that you begin to appreciate the cost of infection in terms of low vitality and indifference. Simple wellness is an immeasurable gift, and without it thoughts about how to achieve health may be still-born. Enough hygiene is a pre-condition for health.

Nevertheless, wellness is not enough. It is the pioneers of community development who are beginning to change our ideas about how medicine fits into the movement of a people towards health.

When I was in Northern Nigeria in 1946 I visited a rural development scheme at Anchau which was directed by the Colonial Medical Services.[52] The scheme began with the intention of eradicating sleeping-sickness from the area. Because the tsetse fly which carries the disease breeds in the shade along river banks, a systematic slashing of the undergrowth was undertaken. It was essential to maintain this work, when completed. But in order that the work of regular scrub clearance each year might not become too great a burden on local farmers, it became necessary to concentrate the population in certain areas. This meant that it would then be possible to maintain the clearance by doing two days slashing a year—a reasonable burden of work for a farmer.

In order to concentrate the population various villages were moved, and this set in train a whole series of activities which affected every aspect of the villagers' lives. Soil and water surveys were done, crop tests, and new designs for houses within the traditional style. By a simple construction of the new well heads, people were prevented from walking in the water hole, and so Guinea Worm was also eliminated from 600 square miles of territory—a parasite of particular malignancy to farmers because it incapacitates them during the wet season when they should be tilling the farm: consequently it impoverishes their families.

In order to help people to understand the changes, schools for literacy were begun so that health education could be carried out. The Anchau rural development scheme is a good example of enlightened preventive medicine (the curative element was small) which took seriously the pattern of a people's life as promoting illness or wellness and health. The directors also took seriously local responsibility for the village communities maintaining their own progress, and the need to change attitudes, customs and beliefs about diet, farming, marketing meat and many other aspects of their lives. Nevertheless, the scheme was devised by Western experts and without them could not have been carried out: this was the era of colonial government before the independence of Nigeria. The development of these Northern villages was an example of progressive preventive medicine followed to its political conclusion.

Today there are many similar schemes throughout the world. Community development may start in many corners of a community's life—with the building of an adventure playground, communal feeding of children, after-school activities, the building of a community centre or a dam for irrigation, or adult education. It is not necessarily concerned with medical or nursing services even in the third world where there is so much illness: often food is the first concern.[53] Community development is nearer to a model of health care because it is concerned not only with the basic necessities of life, but also with the people's struggle to obtain them and enjoy them together.

Health is closely linked to political decisions about priorities—the things in life such as education, transport, food, farming, opportunities for celebration—to which resources of money and manpower will be given. In community development people are making value choices about what they think makes good community life together. They share in decisions: they work together to put their plans into effect, and this co-operation in itself is part of what it is to be a healthy community. People in fact choose what 'health', a healthy life, a healthy society, should mean for them. It is a reflection of their social values.

Nevertheless community development can be a new and more subtle form of imperialism, of cultural invasion, of dehumanising people. Expert community development does not guarantee health. The influence of Western materialism or the leadership of Western doctors who have not overcome in themselves the fear of death, may result in the development of a Western appetite for hygiene, in the growth of a competitive society.

In 1971 the Church Officers of the Evangelical Church

Mekane Yesus in Ethiopia wrote to the donor agencies in Germany and other countries. They said:[54]

We talk today about 'rich' and 'poor' nations, about 'developed' and 'underdeveloped' or 'developing' societies and even of the 'Third World'. In doing this we are using only generally adopted socio-economic measurements to determine which society is rich or poor, developed or underdeveloped. The standard of human life and that of society is normally evaluated in terms of economic growth and material wealth or in technology and production. Based on this materialistic Western concept of development and in an effort to find a remedy at least two things seem to have been largely overlooked, namely:

(a) that there are values in life beyond those of modern technology and economic betterment without which man's development will never be meaningful and lasting.

(b) that man is not only the suffering creature who needs help but that he is also the most important development agent.

In our view a one-sided material development is not only self-deceiving in the sense that man needs more than that, but it is also a threat to the very values which make life meaningful if carried out without due attention to a simultaneous provision to meet spiritual needs.

We know that we need more of modern technology. . . .

However, when we in effect are told, by virtue of criteria unilaterally decided by the Donor Agencies, what we need and what we do not need, what is good for us and what is not good, then we feel uncomfortable and become concerned about our own future.

Looking at the so-called developed societies we realise that in the midst of their affluence man is still suffering from all kinds of evil. The values which make life meaningful seem to be in danger of being lost in these societies. It seems to us that what is happening in the affluent part of the world today points to the fact that technology and economic growth beyond the ability of people to control and responsibly use is leading to development in reverse where man has to suffer new evils.

New styles of social development pose particular difficulties for doctors. They require a new style of being a doctor for which a Western medical education may be not merely inadequate, but a hindrance. A surgeon working on Koje Do (an island off Korea) has described at first hand[55] what such a struggle with one's own professional identity may mean for a doctor when he finds his medical training does not fit the needs of the situation. He lists four stages in the transformation of a physician from one style of doctoring to another: recognition, response, trial and tribulation, and *dénouement*.

A good example of the development of an appropriate style of 'being a doctor' and 'being a nurse' is illustrated by the work of Morley with the Under-Five's Clinics in Nigeria.[56] He shows the enormous saving in children's lives which follows the introduction of preventive paediatrics, as compared with curative medicine only based on hospitals. Many changes in outlook are required in those who run these children's clinics.

The traditional pattern of consultation between the doctor on the one hand, and the sick child and its mother on the other hand may be represented in this way:

Mother
and   Doctor
Child

Diagram 3.   Traditional Pattern of Consultation

The new pattern involves a change of outlook (at its most fundamental a new authority structure) in both doctor, nurse and mother/child. It may be represented as follows:

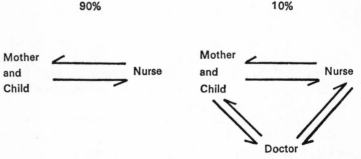

90%   10%

Diagram 4.   Alternative Pattern of Consultation

The nurse (who may have received differing standards of education and training) is not just acting as a filter for the doctor, allowing certain difficult cases through.

Nine out of ten consultations are between the mother and the 'nurse', a locally trained woman who ideally will herself be a mother. She should have five minutes free to spend on each child. All ill children she *herself* accompanies to the doctor. During the 10 per cent of consultations in which the doctor is involved he is making double use of his time by teaching and raising the standard of care offered by the nurse. If he sees that she supervises the treatment he gives he will increase the respect given by the mother to the nurse. . . . To the mothers of sick children the locally trained nurses from their own locality become much the most important people they meet at the hospital. The great importance of the nurse is the really critical factor in the whole psychology of the clinic and is something the doctor does all he can to promote.

The nurse's relationship to the mother is crucial. She carries much more responsibility than is often accorded to a nurse. Likewise the role of the doctor calls for considerable self-effacement, for professional and personal humility. The importance of the doctor's role as teacher is here emphasised. The doctor shares his knowledge with the nurse. The nurse shares her knowledge with the mother, because it is essential to enable people—non-professional amateurs—to be responsible (as far as possible) for their own health care. One of the doctor's prime roles is that of an *enabler* in this process of growth towards maturity, both personal and social.

The use of the nurse in this way is in some ways comparable to the 'practice nurse' in the United Kingdom,[57] and certainly comparable to the role of a midwife. In many countries an increasing use of medical auxiliaries is being made. A useful survey of their value, training and limitations has been published by the Intermediate Technology Development Group.[58] Dr. Katherine Elliott writes:

The medical auxiliary is a substitute, an alternative to a physician in certain special circumstances. The medical auxiliary is not a sub-standard doctor. The medical auxiliary receives a short, practical training. This is often better suited to local educational levels and to the community's immediate needs; it certainly costs considerably less than full professional training as a physician, much of which is theoretical. Expensively trained physicians should be sensibly used in any country. To delegate suitable responsibilities to specially trained auxiliaries is not a detrimental dilution of standards of medical care. An adequate number of well trained auxiliaries properly used must be better value than too few doctors desperately attempting the impossible.

Many examples are given in this book—from the Duke University scheme in North Carolina to the feldshers in the U.S.S.R., as well as others in Africa and China.

The training and use of auxiliaries has not been without opposition.

Perhaps the major medical manpower problem of the world today is how to introduce the medical auxiliary in areas where he is needed, but does not exist, against the widespread opposition of the medical profession.[59] For example, in Pakistan, the licentiate, a medical worker with a shorter period of training, had been taking up many posts in the government rural services which were and are severely understaffed. However, the British General Medical Council did not consider these physicians suitably qualified for practice in the United Kingdom and consequently the occupational group was abolished due to pressure from the Pakistani medical profession, despite the useful work being done by the licentiates. The Pakistani doctors were motivated to an extent by the prospect of being ranked as equals with the licentiates and hence losing their rights to practice in Britain.[60]

Several changes in attitude to health and in the practice of medicine and nursing have been described in relation to community development.

First, the knowledge among deprived and oppressed peoples all over the world that poverty and disease are not inevitable. They now realise that freedom from hunger, war and illness is not only a dream but a possibility, and that a certain standard of hygiene is a human right. The rich and the poor nations, oppressors and oppressed, are more aware of one another and of the affront to justice constituted by the appalling inequity of medical resources.

Secondly, doctors and nurses are in crisis over their professional identity. The specialist in hospital feels this least, the doctor who is closest to the lives of his patients feels this most: and particularly Western trained doctors working in rural areas in the third world. But the whole system of Western medicine and the assumptions on which it is built is misfitted to rapidly changing social needs.

> We must make it clear that there is no ideal medicine, no ideal way of being a doctor, either up in the sky or in the teaching hospitals of the West, waiting to be blue printed on the nations of the world. . . . Doctor excellence is situational. Each tomorrow reveals the nature of the excellence required, whilst at the same time, just as we think we have grasped it, the next tomorrow requires us to learn again a new understanding of excellence.[61]

Thirdly, community development is born among the people themselves. The pattern of development is not induced from outside, but the local people learn to articulate their own needs, take responsibility for development, and may call on outside expertise for advice and help. If the development is imposed by experts, dehumanisation may result in spite of improvement in hygiene.

Fourthly, if people themselves are free to make their own choices, then development will truly reflect their values. They will be working for health—not health after the European pattern but through the enhancement of their own cultural life. Health is perhaps the social milieu which enables each member, individually and jointly, to become more fully human.

GROWTH TOWARDS MATURITY

Not only have doctors in the field of Public Health influenced our ideas of health and styles of medicine and nursing, but the insights of psychiatrists have also changed our understanding of health. The rediscovery of the importance of interpersonal factors in the promotion of health has brought together the ideas of 'health' and 'persons living together in harmony'. Social harmony was the practical aim of the Jewish hope of *Shalom* (literally 'peace').

Not only students of psychiatric illness but observers of human growth and development (eg. the work of Bowlby on maternal deprivation[62] and of Erikson on the stages of human development)[63] have also influenced our concepts of maturity. Many writers who have described psychological models of the 'healthy man' (such as the 'individuation' of Jung, the 'courage to be oneself' of Tillich or the 'mature dependence' of Fairbairn) focus on the individual. Nevertheless sociologists, social psychiatrists and research workers in group dynamics have studied man in his corporate context and shown us that in order to understand health and illness we must pay attention as much to the family, society and culture which mould a man, as to the individual. Indeed, 'There is no such thing as being a separate person'. Health is interpersonal.

A whole new range of components of health have become overt, and some may be represented in the following diagram:[64]

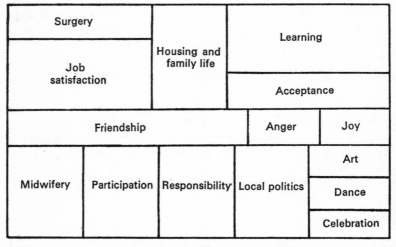

Diagram 5. Interpersonal Components of Health

In diagram 5 some of the earthy components like Surgery,

Midwifery and Housing are retained to remind us that mental health is not a viable concept apart from bodily health: health is interpersonal, both physical and mental.

Psychiatrists have introduced a new cluster of criteria for the evaluation of individual and social well-being with profound effects on our ideas of health. We must now include inter-personal factors such as acceptance or prejudice, ability to adapt to social change, attitudes to old age and death, and the stability of marriage and family life in our evaluation of the health of a society. These criteria can be seen to contain ethical assumptions. Lambourne wrote:[65]

> (These criteria) will not be socio-economic but will be concerned with what are considered to be desirable personal and interpersonal qualities. (Probably these will tend to be denoted in recognisably psychological terminology and supposedly legitimated by psychological science whereas in the past centuries they were denoted in recognisably ethical terminology and supposedly legitimated by theology. Comprehensive mental care practices will inevitably disseminate views about what is the best way of living our lives. These views will be highly conditioned by the brand of humanism congenial to the professionals who develop them.)

Psychiatrists, by introducing interpersonal factors into medicine, have brought the concept of love into health. Man's search for this love which can give him a sense of identity and enhance the quality of his family and social life, is changing the pattern of illness in Britain. Men as men are not satisfied with hygiene: hygiene alone is not enough.

CHANGES IN THE PATTERN OF ILLNESS

In the United Kingdom during the last ten years there has been a striking growth of social services. There has also been a multiplication of voluntary societies concerned with social dis-eases: e.g. the Samaritans (suicide), the Richmond Fellowship (mental illness), the Cyrenians (vagrants), the Cruse Club (widows), Alcoholics and Gamblers Anonymous and various societies concerned with addiction, the Society of the Compassionate Friends (parents bereaved of a child), P.N.P. (People not

Psychiatry, a befriending organisation), Cancer Anonymous, and many other organisations.

The mark of all these agencies, both state and voluntary, is long-term personal care given to those in need by volunteers. Voluntary helpers may or may not receive training; training is very variable in standard: but all require an ability to continue in relationship with others even at cost to themselves. Without this gift, even sophisticated training will fail to produce that which the ill person seeks.

However deeply the conquest of disease appeals to our imagination, however brilliant our technology, there are whole areas of illness which do not yield to our skills. I think most people would say that the areas which defy technical solution are getting smaller. My own view is that they are getting larger —that medical technologists today are, as it were, clearing away the undergrowth, only to reveal realms in which human need is expressed differently.

What is it men seek in their sickness? Cure, of course. But there are signs that deep in his being man knows that even heart transplants are not enough. We need one another's service: we also need one another.

Is there a man among you who will offer his son a stone when he asks for bread?[66]

In illness we do not seek cure alone, but in illness as in wellness we seek one another in relationship. We wish to love and be loved. If we offer one another technology instead (we may, of course, offer both love and technology) then we dehumanise one another. It may be easier to give a widow sleeping pills than to listen to her story and share her tears.

Our understanding of illness does not permit us to see it simply as a sudden event discontinuous with the past. However sudden the coronary thrombosis it does not happen 'out of the blue': years of sick living have gone into its making; it is the cumulative effect of competitive stress, overwork, obesity, diet or family factors, often a complex mixture of more than one cause. The nervous breakdown that hits a middle-aged man is rooted in the emotional problems of his own (or even his parents' or grandparents') childhood decades earlier. The car crash, apparently so random, may be the outcome of personal idiosyncrasies and feelings which, in a given situation, are bound to cause disasters that (though we now know better) we still call accidents.

Only recently have doctors begun to advise businessmen on how they should live or work in order to prevent the incidence of sickness in the pre-retiring and early post-retirement years. We are changing from a hospital-orientated pattern of curing diseases (which may themselves be symptoms of sick living) to a preventive pattern of medicine influenced by our understanding of ways of life as sickness-producing or health-enhancing. This is a development that depends less on the skills of technology and more on sociological insights. It is a new discipline of 'whole person' medicine which sees a wide range of medical/social problems such as accident-proneness, addiction, vagrancy, violence—as symptoms of the family and social conditions in which people live. People in social and interpersonal crises require continuing care which hospitals are not designed to give. In addition it is not always clear why one man goes to prison, another to a psychiatric institution and a third finds help through a social work agency. It is possible to sit in court and hear a magistrate with a punitive outlook sentencing men in the morning; and in the same court in the afternoon there is a magistrate with a quite different outlook who leaves no stone unturned to help men towards rehabilitation.

Hospitals, especially those where future physicians are trained, are highly selective institutions. There is a tidiness about them that puts beyond the pale those many sick people who will not conform in their symptomatology and cannot or will not go sick in ways which fit the hospital pigeon-holes.

Is it then meaningful to speak of many of these people as ill? What is illness? If a man breaks a leg in a car crash, or develops pneumonia he is likely to turn to a doctor for help. He is certified sick, receives sick benefit, and probably gets treatment in hospital. On return to work he will get nothing but sympathy. His condition is socially acceptable.

If a man has a nervous breakdown or drinks heavily we may have considerable doubt as to whether his behaviour is morally reprehensible or due to illness. Shame, embarrassment and secrecy may surround the behaviour. The question of a person's responsibility for his behaviour is assessed in widely different ways, 'He ought to pull his socks up', implying that he *can* do so. Or, 'He is sick and not responsible for his actions'.

There are conditions even further from socially sanctioned norms which are described as 'deviant' behaviour, such as vagrancy or drug dependence. Some deviants are people who opt out of the way of life generally approved of in society. Many are rejected by their families, or choose to live alone in cities: others are highly social. All over western Europe more and more young people refuse to live a materialistic and competitive kind of life. They prefer to adopt their own style of dress, common life and public celebrations. Some opt out of society in a passive way: others remain within society but protest actively. Among such people are sources of hope and development for the future. Unable or unwilling to adapt to Western culture, they may well contribute different qualities to a new society in which many who now conform will feel equally ill-adapted.

To attempt to label deviant people as 'ill' is a way of re-assuring myself that I who conform am 'well'. But hippies think it is we who are 'sick'. Indeed in many ways Western society is sick. But the use of the word 'sick' indicates how much we respect the power of doctors to cure and control, to restore to normality and to conformity those who disturb our peace of mind. It is often said that patients are admitted to psychiatric hospital more for the sake of society than for the sake of the patient. Behaviour which is considered unacceptable in one culture may be normal in another. Our behaviour is sanctioned or rejected by our own neighbours. Our personal attitudes to illness are moulded by those with whom we live and work.

In Britain the extent to which demand for medical care is dependent on personal attitudes rather than morbidity is illustrated by the statistics of absence from work attributed to sickness. It has been shown that there can be a threefold difference in the numbers of spells of absence in groups with comparable morbidity.[67]

Less and less do orthodox doctors trained in Western teaching hospitals practise a style of medicine which is able to help men and women who fall victims to the stresses and pressures of Western culture. The technological role which doctors have taken up in the last twenty-five years no longer fits the social context in which medicine has to be practised. The ways in which most people today become sick increasingly by-pass a system of medicine based on cure of disease. The treatment of disease is too manipulative an approach to be acceptable to those who seek a personal model of healing.

The traditional situation is one in which the doctor is well, upright, mobile, uniformed (white coat) and gives 'doctor's orders' to the patient (i.e. the passive one) who is ill, prone, bed-fast and often in hospital clothes. This situation which is in some ways appropriate for a surgical ward, is not merely inappropriate but dehumanising in most doctor/patient situations. A new relationship is being sought between helper and helped in which without denying the expertise of the helper and the need of the helped, the helped also has something to give to the helper. Their meeting is more in the nature of a dance together than a traditional consultation. This is further discussed (page 51) in relation to Community Therapy Units.

Because of the changes of the pattern of illness in the West there is already a response by society to people's needs through the development of social work and voluntary agencies. This means two things:

(a) That the first assessor of dis-ease (apart from the patient himself and his family), traditionally a general medical practitioner (a G.P.), may not need to be primarily a medical man. He might more appropriately be someone trained in the community and having an outlook more akin to a social worker, rather than a doctor trained in a hospital. For many different reasons, sick people seek a personal relationship. Estimates vary but it would probably be accepted that more than half the illness in Great Britain is predominantly emotional and behavioural. This is a more significant change in the pattern of illness than the obvious fact that in hospital wards there are now so many elderly patients.

In the hospital where I worked in Africa the pattern of illness is dominated by tropical infections, parasites and poverty. Many of these diseases are easily recognisable (my first African patient, a boy of eight, told me that he had Bilharzia!). In Great Britain the obvious major infections of this kind have been overcome both by treatment and preventive measures. The pattern of illness is quite different, because our style of life is different. Much of our illness today is related to the effects of stress on the harmony of the personality. In Western culture, therefore, the primary 'trouble-shooter' needs *first* to be competent in the understanding of personal and family emotional disturbance. (This is further discussed on page 97.)

(*b*) The change in the pattern of illness and the response by society which I have described also means that there is a protest developing against too much specialisation and professionalism. By referring people in need of neighbourly help to the expert we can deprive ourselves of ordinary simple opportunities to care for one another, and soon cease to care. There are documented examples[68] of incidents where ordinary citizens have failed to go to the assistance of another citizen in urgent need of help. At best we fetch an Ambulance: 'they' will cope. At worst we pass by on the other side.

As specialisation proceeds inevitably in Western society, there is at the same time a reappreciation of simple neighbourliness. It is not certain at present whether many voluntary societies will be seduced into a clinical approach to human problems or will continue to offer opportunities for good neighbourliness which is the very cement of life-together. Without such good neighbourliness, we all get further and further away from our neighbours, like the citizens of C. S. Lewis' hell.[69] Without such mutual support at neighbourhood level, it is very doubtful if we can maintain the present high level of care for old people in the community, in their own or their families' homes. With the best will in the world a family may not be able to care for the grandparents unless local support is available. The professionalisation of care has the inevitable effect of collecting those who need care into institutions run by professionals. And the creation of old people's Homes inevitably influences the way we think about caring for the elderly.

Members of the voluntary organisations, such as those that we have mentioned, could play a more conscious part in increasing neighbourly care in the community by deliberately training more volunteers than they require; and fitting them both to help those in trouble and to promote health in those among whom they live and work.

There is, then, in Western culture, a change in the pattern of illness, and a change in the response of society to it. It could be that the search for a friend which I have described, is not simply a search for care and relief from anxiety, depression and the symptoms of alienation and loss of identity so rife in Britain, but a search for meaning, for quality of life, for values other than materialist, and for a chance to develop our humanity together, in fact a search for health.

THE COMMUNITY THERAPY UNIT[70]

It has often been noted[71] that in a psychiatric hospital patients receive support and insight from one another. One of the most sensitive accounts of this is in the novel 'I never promised you a Rose Garden'.[72] This continues, in a different way, one of the themes of the last section (Changes in the pattern of Illness), namely that our hope of liberation and growth towards maturity lies in our immediate relationships to one another, and not only with the expert. To turn to an outside expert may alienate us still further unless he can help us to return for help to the very situation which seems to threaten us.

The community therapy unit grew out of the realisation that when a mentally ill patient is admitted to hospital, it is not only the skilled help of medical and nursing staff which restores his/her balance, but that all the relationships in the hospital— the complete 'family life' of the institution—are conducive to illness or recovery. This means that the relationships between different professions on the staff, doctor, nurse, social worker, administrator, as well as between staff and patients and between patients themselves are significant for the progress or regress of all.

In a community therapy unit, therefore, a conscious effort is made to make use of all the potentialities of both staff and patients in one whole treatment programme. The structure of the unit is devised to enable each individual member to share his or her own gift, skill or experience with others.

One change in this type of unit is that patients are much more fully consulted about the details of everyday life that affect them so closely. A sense of responsibility is developed which goes a long way to prevent the onset of institutionalisation, a grave condition of deterioration in humanity.

Another change which the pioneers of therapeutic communities have brought about in psychiatric hospitals has been a new freedom: locked doors are rare, many patients go home for the weekend and church services are voluntary and no longer a disciplined parade! Because feelings may be expressed and understood rather than repressed there has been a diminishment in violent and bizarre behaviour which was more a product of the padded cell and custodial atmosphere than the illness itself:[73]

> Perhaps the most important realisation brought home to us by our study of the old system and by information from our patients, was that in the past we have been treating people as things, or, at best, as interesting diseases. Somehow we had lost our way in giving pride of place to the inherent value of persons. When this happens, the end begins to justify the means and many measures were used in order to control the disturbed behaviour of mental illness, much of it produced by the system itself which denied the fundamental importance of recognising our patients as people with rights, opinions and feelings that we should respect. A vicious circle was then too easily established. A system which tends to create tensions and disturbed behaviour was called upon to suppress and control these by the same measures that originally helped to produce them. Heavier and heavier sedation, repeated courses of E.C.T. had to be used in many wards to maintain some sort of control over the more difficult patients who did not readily submit to hospital life. Little attempt was made to understand the behaviour in terms of the patient's human response to the total situation of ward and hospital life. It was through our experimental community units that we learned at first hand how wrong it is to assume that the mentally ill cannot act as people in their own right and make a real contribution to their own treatment. Often they were able to tell us, directly or indirectly, how wrong we had been in many assumptions about their needs.

The basis of the therapeutic community is a regular ward meeting of all patients and staff—including non-professional staff—at which there is free and undirected discussion. Matters related to the organisation of the unit, domestic affairs, and the emotional problems and feelings of individuals as well as interpersonal relationships may be discussed. The meetings in this way also provide material for group therapy.

Another most striking change which this type of unit is

bringing about in some psychiatric hospitals is in the concept of authority. This is symbolised in the lack of staff uniforms. It may be difficult for a newcomer to discover at his first ward meeting who are staff and who are patients. The strength of the community may lie in the fact that everyone is given a voice, and attention is paid to what he/she says. It is the assumption 'that the person in authority knows best' that the members of the community rightly challenge. Such a change is not necessarily complete, nor achieved without anxiety or cost.[74] Nevertheless the change has begun and the best Community Therapy Units are working for health as well as wellness. It is to be hoped that the lessons will spread to other types of hospital. The doctors, nurses and patients who are still pioneering new ways to become more fully human have the one essential quality—courage.

In the context of a therapeutic community doctors and nurses undergo a painful change in their professional identity. A doctor's job is highly skilled. He is carefully selected, rigorously trained and enjoys strong professional support in hospital. His work is very fulfilling and his status is in high social regard. Few stand on a higher pedestal. It is difficult to imagine how threatened a psychiatrist feels when he consents to sit in a circle of chairs with patients and listens to their criticism of (for example) his high-handed way of moving his patients from ward to ward. The professional identity in which he felt secure comes under severe question. Who is he? What skills has he to offer? Can he bear to continue in a relationship in which he is vulnerable? If he becomes a man who is learning things from his patients, what kind of authority does he exercise as a doctor?

Much emotional illness can be seen to be a family affair. Husband and wife obviously affect one another's well-being. Their children can become ill if the relationship between husband and wife is insecure. Siirala[75] has described how 'the nest' in which a child is nurtured can make all the difference to the development of a child's ability to talk. He gives case histories of children whose brains have been damaged at birth in the area responsible for speech. Acceptance or rejection of the child by its parents may make all the difference between the child's learning to communicate or becoming dumb. The work in psychiatric hospitals is beginning to reflect this corporate understanding of illness. Some hospitals (the Cassel Hospital near London is an example in the United Kingdom) admit the whole family to special family units. A doctor or social worker visits them for family discussions. By talking about their difficulties and their feelings members of a family can be helped to communicate with one another more openly, to understand, and to grow more mature.

Family therapy, as it is called, is now beginning to find its way into general practice, and a general practitioner, social worker or practice nurse may make a point of meeting with a whole family where illness cannot realistically be seen to be one member's full responsibility. Family therapy is not a panacea, but experiments from Colorado State Psychiatric Hospital[76] suggest that it may be more economical in terms of work days lost and days spent in hospital if acute mental illness is seen as a family crisis. Clinical attention is given to the whole family at home rather than being focused on an individual's psychotic episode as an event which requires his admission to hospital.

The changes taking place in this area may be summarised as follows:

(i) Emotional illness is now being understood less in individual terms and more as a family, a group, even a social manifestation. It is not just an individual who is anxious or depressed; he presents the symptoms of defective interpersonal relationships between himself and others, between the members of his family, his peer group, his tribe, his nation. His family is sick in him. There is therefore a change taking place in the actual way that we now perceive mental illness.

(ii) In an institution like a psychiatric hospital, a patient is not an individual sick person who has been isolated for treatment. He/she becomes a member of a community in which the day to day life is either liberating or oppressing. The interpersonal relationships between patients and staff, staff and staff, staff and relatives, patients and patients, patients and relatives make up a whole milieu in which all ('ill' and 'well') may give and receive, learn and grow, or withdraw and 'die'.

(iii) This situation calls for a change of self-identity and of professional self-image among staff, a very painful process of unlearning and relearning how to be a doctor, or a nurse. A hospital is a place for truth.

(iv) Reciprocally, patients are having to learn painfully what it means to be responsible agents. Between patients and doctors a new mode of exercising authority is being worked out. He who is willing to be vulnerable, to share experience, and to deploy skills in understanding human behaviour, is respected as an authentic person. To be the recipient of the benefits of another's skill may be a personalising or depersonalising experience. Less and less does technique alone give a man respected status.

This pattern of co-operation is now beginning to influence the 'general' hospital. For example, a 'continuing care unit' has been established as an experiment in the Thayer Hospital, Waterville, U.S.A.[77] In this unit the patient and staff both inside and outside the hospital work together on plans for the long-term readaptation of patients to their situations. Re-adaptation is not something which a hospital does for its patients; it is a joint response to a situation in life (such as a handicap due to a stroke) which patients and professionals make together.

The mechanistic approach to health as manifested in the technology of the National Health Service is now visibly inadequate. There is no way to health through the cure of illness. Indeed we can no longer maintain the old *clinical* distinction between 'wellness' and 'illness' upon which the Health Service is based. Rather than trying to reach health by understanding illness, we must first try to understand health, in the light of which we may be able to say something about being well or ill.

The components of health still exist in society and are the same as they always were. The changes in structure and practice which we have described in this section gain their strength from the growth of new roots which go down to the depth of human experience and re-extract those elements of life from which health grows—elements such as love, justice, openness to learning by experience, courage to assume a new identity, and willingness to suffer together for the sake of long-term objectives. Practical examples of what this may mean both for doctors and society have been described.

Health is situational, that is, it is related to what a people believes to be fullness of life for them. It is an expression of qualities to which they give value, and because they must choose between different factors in a world of limited resources, ethico/political decisions are involved. Health is evaluated by many criteria drawn from every corner of a people's life, including their capacity for enriching interpersonal relationships.

PART III

Becoming More Fully Human

HEALTH IS A HUMAN POSSIBILITY

There is an African fable about a farmer who brought home a chick from an eagle's eyrie.[78] Not quite knowing what to do with it, he put it in a chicken run, where it grew up with the chickens. One day a passing traveller saw it, and commented on its presence. 'It's a chicken,' said the farmer: 'Not so,' said the traveller, 'it's an eagle.' And he took it on his wrist and spoke to the great bird. 'You're an eagle,' he said. 'Fly!' But the eagle looked down at the chickens in the run, hopped down and pecked with them. 'You see,' said the farmer, 'I told you so. It's a chicken.'

For the next week the traveller called each day and brought such food as is proper to an eagle, raw meat and flesh. Slowly the bird's strength began to revive.

So again the traveller took the bird on his wrist and spoke to it: 'You're an eagle,' he said. 'Fly!' and the great bird stretched his wings, but when he saw the chickens in the run, he hopped down and scratched with them. 'You're wasting your time,' said the farmer, 'I told you. It's a chicken.'

Next morning while it was still dark the traveller returned, and taking the bird on his wrist he walked a little way into the bush. As the morning sun rose and tipped with a golden light the great crag where the eagles' eyrie was built, he lifted the bird and pointed to the mountain top: 'You're an eagle,' he said. 'Fly!' And the great bird looked up to the top of the crag, stretched his wings and flew, round and round and round ... until he vanished in the sky.

57

Christ enables us to become what we already are. cf. doctor + the elephant man.

The life of a chicken is sufficient for a chicken, but the life of a chicken spells death for an eagle. Aggrey of Africa told and retold this story to African audiences (1920–21). He made them aware of their latent gifts for leadership and responsibility which could be realised through the African struggle for freedom.

Aggrey points to the heart of health as possibility. We are tempted to live at the level of supply and demand, but this is to deny our true humanity. Man cannot live on bread alone.[79] Certainly we are creatures with basic needs. Because of our creatureliness we must have bread and water and air and vitamins and warmth and shelter . . . but to live humanly these are not enough. Man cannot be human by satisfaction of his biological needs alone. The Shona people speak of *unhu*, as the basis of personhood or community spirit—human worth.

An African from one of the South African territories spoke in Birmingham of the freedom fighters in prison: 'They make,' he said, 'an enclave of liberation and human dignity within those prisons.' This remark points to the existence of a quality of life amid conditions which might well have denied its flowering: to the existence of certain *human* qualities, which are distinct from our animal wants and not always dependent on their being satisfied.

HEALTH IS AN ADVENTURE

In his research on job satisfaction and job dissatisfaction in industry Hertzberg[80] noted two distinct sets of factors:

(i) those concerned with job dissatisfaction he described as *hygiene* factors. They are related to the conditions in which the work is done, such as wages, hours of work and canteen facilities. The hygiene factors are thus related to creaturely comforts or biological necessities. When they are met satisfactorily, however, you do not then have job satisfaction, you simply have *not* got job dissatisfaction. No attention to hygiene factors produces job satisfaction. Indeed hygiene factors have a tendency to recur in the same or different forms.

(ii) Job satisfaction is related to the nature of the work, and these factors Hertzberg called *motivators*. They are concerned with a sense of achievement, and with responsibility. The motivators are thus concerned with humanness, not simply biological factors. If these motivators are missing, you do not have job dissatisfaction you simply have *not* got job satisfaction.

I wish to make a comparable distinction between hygiene and health. Our present idea of health is better represented by the word wellness (page 4). The National Health Service is concerned to make and keep us well. (It will be referred to in future as the NHS because to call it a National Health Service, when it is not, is confusing.) The NHS, then, is one of a constellation of services which provide hygiene—the basic essentials for our existence. We must have food, water, medicines, clothing and housing. These requirements are similar to Hertzberg's 'hygiene factors'. They are set out in the United Nations Charter—freedom from want, from fear, from war, from ignorance and from disease. But when these human desires are met, we do not have health. Health is still a further possibility.

Health is concerned with a different set of factors related to humanness, to human relations in community. These factors which make for health are comparable to Hertzberg's 'motivators' and are concerned with a sense of personal and social identity, human worth, communication, participation in the making of political decisions, celebration and responsibility.

Hertzberg further sharpened the distinction between his two sets of factors by describing them as related to the 'Adam' nature of man—man as a creature among other creatures. And to the 'Abraham' nature of man—man as the adventurer who left his home 'knowing not whither he went', to seek a more fully human way of life even at risk to himself and his companions.

Maslow[81] has described human needs in the form of a hierarchy which develops during growth through childhood and adolescence. He suggests that the next higher need only impinges upon someone when their lower needs have been met. He described five requirements in order as follows:

1. Physiological, e.g. Food and water
2. Safety, e.g. Protection from harm
3. Social, e.g. Affection, sense of worth
4. Esteem, e.g. Self-respect, success
5. Need for self-actualisation

The NHS therefore sets out to provide wellness. This is a physiological or Adam factor, one part of hygiene. In underdeveloped countries we have described how essential wellness is as a preliminary liberation for populations rendered apathetic by disease. Wellness may—but only *may*, a possibility not a certainty—purvey values beyond itself in terms of quickened consciousness and social development.

Hygiene is related to the basic necessities of biological life. Health points to our human potential measured in terms of quality of life, individual, national and international. Health is a word related to the quality of human life in ecological terms, that is, it is not just an individual quality, but is related to life lived together in harmony with the environment. Hygiene is therefore a foundation for other qualities of life.

It is clear therefore that health is complex, and no single definition can serve our purpose. Only manifold descriptions can do justice to its richness. The voices of artist, dramatist, politician, housewife, and the mother of a family are as authentic as those of doctor, nurse and social worker, in that all have human experience and vision to contribute. The language of science alone is insufficient to describe health: the languages of story, myth and poetry also disclose its truth. Any conference on health must be as widely representative of human genius as possible. Health is a symbolic word (in the sense of 'bringing together'): we cannot understand health by analysing it (breaking it down) only by building its different facets together. Health is then found to be a greater whole than the simple sum of its parts.

An abstract definition may not be possible, but we can recognise health when we see it. The individual writer like myself, therefore, can only explore the area of health with others and make such descriptions as are possible. I would wish to describe health as I recognise it in many different situations.

GIVING, RECEIVING AND SHARING

I was brought up in the Potteries in the days of desperate poverty, the 1920s and early 1930s. I have sat next to children in school who were barefoot in all weathers. I have worked in Africa and seen the lavish use of a tapped water supply in modern bungalows and gardens, while a few miles away the women, with rusty petrol cans on their heads, trek to dirty water-holes infested with bilharzia and guinea worm. There is competition for natural resources.

Men compete for food, for housing, for raw materials, for oil, for the basic necessities of life. Some have too much and some have too little. It is common knowledge that two-thirds of the world's population have insufficient to eat: while obesity is a common clinical problem among the remaining third. For millions of people poverty so saps their energy and condemns them to apathy that even to live as a well-fed chicken would seem health indeed.

In the time of the Great Unemployment in the Potteries you might notice how thin and pale the mother of a family grew for the sake of her children. In parts of Asia and Africa it is only too obvious that the birth of another child means less food to go round. In terms of hygiene resources my brother is my rival. He is another mouth to feed. That means less for me. In the United Kingdom there are not enough kidney transfusion machines to go round. There is competition for hygiene, for the resources which keep Adam alive.

In Part II (page 17) we described the contrast between the luxury of resources required to effect a heart transplant in Cape Town, with the poverty of resources in Zululand in the same country. In 1967[82] there was one doctor for every 640 people in Europe: in Africa, one doctor for every 9,700. The fair distribution of resources through hygiene services is one of the major ethical problems in the world.

In the United Kingdom the advertisements for private medical insurance offer privacy, personal attention and queue jumping as advantages which can be bought. Those of us who have known someone close to us suffering because there was no hospital bed available, and who had been told that of course if they liked to have the matter dealt with privately . . . will know that it is our sense of injustice which is roused. We compete, in fact, for hygiene resources. Anyone who is able to say 'I have enough' or 'I am well' must then go on to ask 'At cost to whom have I enough?' 'At cost to whom am I well?'

The fair distribution of hygiene, of food, medical and nursing treatment, of the basic necessities of life is a matter of social justice. Many different visions of the just society have stipulated—'To each according to his need . . .'

However, giving men what they require does not necessarily

see poem in notes

61

bring health. The provision of hygiene cannot satisfy Abraham appetites. In Western society many hospital patients receive every care for their biological needs, without human care.

In West Africa there was a leper settlement just outside a big city where the kindness of the local citizens slowly but surely reduced the lepers to beggars. Simone Weil writes:[83]

We have invented the distinction between justice and charity. It is easy to understand why. Our notion of justice dispenses him who possesses from the obligation of giving. If he gives all the same, he thinks he has a right to be pleased with himself. He thinks he has done a good work. As for him who receives, it depends on the way he interprets this notion whether he is dispensed from all gratitude, or whether it obliges him to offer servile thanks.

Giving can hurt. Caring can patronise. The effects on both giver and receiver are dehumanising when the gift which justice should provide as a matter of common humanity masquerades as charity from the 'haves' to the 'have-nots'. Sometimes the only way charity can be expressed is through justice. It is somewhere here that I recognise a difference between health and hygiene.

Berdyaev wrote:[84]

Bread for myself is a material question: bread for my neighbour is a spiritual question.

By this I understand that the only way to evade the effects of competition is by sharing. To share my loaf with my brother is to acknowledge his body's hunger as equal to my own: it is also to confirm the reality of his brotherhood to me, and to show that I value his destiny as I value my own. This is health for us both. But it depends upon having a loaf to share—by which I mean that health is solidly related to material things. Man may not be able to live by bread alone, but he clearly cannot exist without it.

To argue that health is more than meeting basic human necessities for food and clothing and shelter, is not to devalue these basic necessities. It is in fact to suggest that the material necessities of life—biologically essential for our very existence—

can be a further means of enhancing our humanness. We can no more exist without food than we can exist without bodies; within our present experience both food and bodies are essential for human relationships, for adventure and dance.

You can feed a bedfast patient in two ways—biologically and humanly. You can change his wet bed in two ways, mechanically and personally. Not all nurses have welcomed their relief from non-nursing duties, because it is in and through such chores that nurses may both get to know and express their care for their patients. (I am aware this is a complex situation, I am making one simple point and I would not wish to give the impression that this is all that could be said on the matter.)

We do not compete for health in the way we compete for hygiene. Health is not for the rich to give to the poor. Health is a quality of life they make together. Neither can possess health apart from the other, nor one steal health from the other without robbing himself. Rich and poor, doctor and patient, oppressor and oppressed make one another healthy or unhealthy. Health is non-competitive.

Nevertheless it is not just food, medicine and other materials which are shared. In some way they are also the vehicle for human interchange. In sharing my loaf with another I may meet not only his hunger for food but also his hunger for a brother. Health is about sharing, sharing what we have with one another, and sharing ourselves with one another. Health is about our relationship to material things, and our relationship to one another. We make health possible for one another.

LIFE IS DOMINANT OVER DEATH

Some live dying: best to die living (E. J. Stieglitz).

In Part I (page 28) we discussed the assumption underlying hospital medicine, that 'Death is the worst thing that can happen to a man'.

We may speak of death in two ways. A scientist speaks of a biological process or event which terminates life; death is a precise statement about reality. A poet, on the other hand, uses the word 'death' as a symbol to convey the reality itself; the word death points with sharp imagery to decay and ending in personal and social life, in heart, mind, body or community.

In the Bible the word 'death' is used in both these ways, factual and symbolic:

There was Sisera lying dead with the tent-peg in his skull[85]

is a factual statement of decease.

This son of mine was dead and has come back to life; he was lost and is found,[86]

is a sharp image of the experience of both the prodigal son in a far-off country, and of the father waiting at home. It does not refer to his biological death but to the death of separation from his father and his home and to the degradation of his way of life in the far-off country.

Our use of the word 'dead' may mean the end of a life, a tribe, a civilisation. Or it may be used of an unfruitful womb, of extrusion from a human group, of a church which has lost its mission, of a bushman languishing in a South African gaol cut off from his tribal stories. In medieval Europe the burial service was said over a patient admitted to a leper's institution, and a gallows hung over the gate.

'In the midst of life we are in death.' Yes, indeed, we know that in every cell of our bodies there is a finely balanced process of building and destroying. Yet it is more than that. Our lives are limited: death throws its shadow forward. My death is a present reality; *now* I am living with the knowledge of my mortality. This fact affects my present style of life. 'Farm', says a Herefordshire saying, 'as if you were going to live for ever. Live as if you were going to die tomorrow.'

(1) *Birth, Life and Death*

Western fears of death are chiefly related to the biological threat of expiry at the end of life, not to the symbolic patterns of deadly behaviour amid daily existence: to quantity of life, not quality. There is little poetry in the Western way of life.

Because death is feared as a biological process or an event at the end of life, one way to draw its sting is to accord it its evolutionary significance. In 1859 Darwin described his theory of the *Origin of Species* through natural selection. This undermined the idea that man was a particular creation separate from the rest of the animal kingdom. It introduced a vast new

64

time-scale into the concept of creation, and gave to death a prime significance in the whole creative process. Teilhard de Chardin has called death 'the essential lever in the mechanism and upsurge of life'. It is death which enables new forms better adapted to the environment or with rich possibilities for life, to develop. The brief life of the Fairy Shrimp[87] which perishes in millions when the shallow pools on Dartmoor dry up in the summer, is only possible because the shrimps lay eggs which resist desiccation whereas its voracious enemies cannot survive in such temporary waters. The mass death of fairy shrimps is the secret of their capacity for life. Life and death are intertwined. Without death on a scale which beggars the imagination, man would not have been born.

The whole nature of human sexuality, and the bearing of children owes its existence to death. For it is only mortal men and women who require replacements. Death is as much a part of the creation as birth. It is not a 'bad'; even though bitter, we must affirm that it is a 'good'. Death has meaning for the future of man in society. For man through consciousness and speech has been able to transcend a process of evolution which, prior to man, was greatly dependent on genes. Man's genetic development is far outstripped in speed and scope by his social development. For we now pass on to our children a vast amount of social information about what it means to be human, through spoken and written words, through living example.

Death has therefore not merely biological significance but also social significance. Retirement from leadership in the community may be described as a 'death' most necessary for social evolution if the next generation of men and women are to work out in family, national and international life what it means to be human in *their* time, not ours. Death is a self-offering into the future of MAN. But we deny the dying involved in the act of retirement just as we deny dying as a biological event. And if I deny my own death, I deny life to others. Do aged leaders in Church and State bear witness to our fear of death, or to our valuation of human qualities which ripen in the later years?

The whole-hearted acceptance of death is essential for health, both personal and social. Biological death is not just a terminal event, it is a continuous process in life. Every creature in every

65

cell of its body is constantly dying and regenerating. In the same way a whole-hearted acceptance of birth is also essential for the personal and social health of the community. We are losing our sense of wonder at the growing life of the foetus in the womb. From the moment of conception this new life is sensitive, growing in awareness of and communication with its world and ours. We are trying to put all normal deliveries into a hospital context, when it is the home environment that is familiar to mother and foetus. The mother's feel, not that of the nurse, will give the new babe security. So today, at the very start of life, we may deny its full possibilities. Both birth and death are increasingly perceived in mechanical terms rather than as great human occasions full of possibilities for the strengthening of family ties. We need to harness our medical and midwifery resources to let such occasions develop their true value. Too often we sterilise them with our clinical obsessions.

(2) *The symbolic use of the word 'death'*

The psychologist, sociologist, historian and theologian have always made use of poetic imagery to convey the reality of death in the midst of life, rather than death merely as a termination to existence. In life there are patterns of death (spiritual death, death of quality) which are an ending or diminishment of health rather than an ending or diminishment of length of life. A loss of potential, a maiming of body or self, a withering of humanity, a denial of participation, an extrusion, exclusion, banishment, a theft of meaning through denial or oppression: these things are deadly to a man's growth towards maturity, these things spell death. Man cannot live on bread alone.[88] Men may die amid plenty or live fully though dying.

Death in terms of such a loss of quality in life refers to what goes into the years or months or days, their value, their richness: the joy, the human relationships, the sense of worth and being wanted. When these are non-existent, then a person is dead even though eating and sleeping and breathing: qualitatively dead, like an eagle living as a chicken, an old person beautifully 'kept' but rejected, someone living in a new high-rise flat without any community life, a South American peasant impoverished and oppressed. We can murder one another in ways far more brutal than killing.

66

(3) *Social patterns of death*

Inclusion is a pattern of health, *exclusion* a pattern of death (the leper). In social terms a society may 'kill' (may treat in a way which spells death for) those of whom it disapproves, those whom it fears, those by whom it feels itself threatened. So society excludes (kills, sometimes literally) either by its attitudes, by segregation, institutionalisation or execution, the bad, the mad, the black, the widow, the leper, the aged, the underprivileged, the mentally subnormal, the rebel and the dying. This exclusive pattern of dealing with 'pollution' results in a 'safe' and sanitated society, but not a healthy society. We have referred above (page 4) to this negative model of health in current use in the West. It is a model in bondage to the fear of evil and biological death.

Kayper Mensah[89] in his poem 'Imports and Exports' sharply tells how black men may be dehumanised by exclusion in a white society—among our exports are:

Niggers—Made in whiteman's land.

In addition to exclusion, there are other social attitudes which deny men and societies their full development. They also must be recognised as patterns of death.

The work of Paulo Freire[90] in South America illustrates the power of words to awaken oppressed peasants. *Oppression* denies the possibilities of life to those who must continue in poverty and illiteracy. Medicine may unwittingly act as the handmaid of such oppression. Examples were given in Part I (page 23).

Medicine too can encourage a *dependence* which is deadly to human maturity. Because doctors bring skill and knowledge to bear upon particular diseases, their work is bound to be specialised. Doctors are therefore in a 'strong' position relatively to the patient. It is easy for a patient to become dependent upon his doctor and to abrogate all responsibility. 'What you say, doctor.' The doctor may assume authority and the patient become so compliant that we speak easily of 'doctor's orders'. In fact no doctor can give orders to any patient in regard to his treatment or behaviour. He has no more authority over a patient than the patient gives him. In 1972 considerable publicity was given to Sir Francis Chichester because he 'defied doctor's orders' and went to sea for his last journey. An editorial in the *Sunday Express*[91] gives the clue to his character:

> Sir Francis Chichester lived for years in death's shadow. It never troubled him. . . . In the end frailty and death overcame him, but they had no victory. The abiding memory of Sir Francis Chichester is of a man who turned every moment of life into something precious.

He was independent enough to defy those who sincerely sought to save his life, because he had found something greater to give his life to, rather than merely prolonging it.

We must therefore recognise blind *conformity* as one of the influences restrictive to human growth. What it means to be a human being is passed down from one generation to the next in the ways we mentioned when thinking about social evolution. In Christianity, Buddhism, Marxism and other great systems of belief, men hand on their experiences of the truth in doctrines and sayings which every recipient must crack like the husk of a coconut if he is to obtain the milk of its meaning for daily life. Doctrines which are handed on as if they were merely for intellectual acceptance or as measures of conformity may actually restrict our growth by denying us understanding of the life experience which they contain. Doctrines that describe a life-giving experience for one people or one generation may be sources of partial death for other people or another generation. James Mathers in a paper on 'Prejudice'[92] points out how the intense tribal loyalty of the Jews described in the history of the Old Testament, helped their survival as a nation and gave them a strong sense of their own identity. But Christians, whose history begins in Judaism, had to break out of what in a larger context was seen to be a pattern of death—tribal prejudice.

Another form of dependence which is deadly to human maturity is caused by *patronisation*. It is always one of the risks of giving, of giving from a situation of strength, of knowledge, of plenty; such as the giving of skill by professionals like doctors, nurses or social workers, and the giving of funds for development by rich nations and churches. It is hard to give without enslaving both giver and receiver. Olivia Mukuna[93] describes the process of cultural invasion which is one of the most dehumanising aspects of white paternalism.

Cultural invasion, perhaps the most effective tool for oppression, is the imposition by the oppressor of his 'world view' on the oppressed. The oppressor's very strong ethnocentric attitude together with other conquest tactics manages to make the oppressed believe in his 'intrinsic inferiority'. (Early missionary attitude of condemning wholesale everything African as demonic and heathen made a significant contribution to cultural invasion in Africa) ... White or Western values became the standard measure, above all the white skin is a symbol of virtue and beauty (the latter especially exemplified by women using corrosive bleaching creams to make their skins lighter). Black becomes the cursed colour to the extent that God is condemned for having made one black.

Patronisation may in this way spread death. Aggrey of Ghana[94] said:

If I went to heaven and God said: 'Aggrey, I am going to send you back, would you like to go as a white man?' I should reply, 'No, send me back as a black man, yes completely black.' And if God should ask 'Why?' I would reply, 'Because I have a work to do as a black man that no white man can do. Please send me back as black as you can make me.'

This affirmation of African dignity is health. In health, difference is an enrichment, and a healthy community would include both black and white men; unafraid perhaps to acknowledge their prejudice and their differences because made of one blood. We would recognise that what we share in common as men and women is far greater than our differences which then appear as an enrichment, not a source of division. Health is inclusive.

Any description of health must pay attention to such enrichment of inter-personal relationship. But we do not always admit that any increase in our sensitivity to one another also increases our power to hurt one another. Joy and pain are inseparable companions.

must risk ourselves for others

Love hurts

(4) *Life-through-death*

The process of natural growth harbours a pattern of life-through-death. There is so much in the adolescent that must die out if the adult is to be born: childish attitudes and dependence must die if adult responsibility and maturity are to be achieved.

And there is so much middle age to die out, if old age is to be entered in peace and fulfilment. The day a father finds for the first time that his son runs faster than he does, he dies a death! We must value old age not by how much middle age we can retain, but for its own proper fruits and gifts. Physical strength, ambition and power must be allowed to die, if old age is to be free to make its own contributions of tranquillity and wisdom.

The experience of loss is the experience of partial death: and it is through facing loss that we learn to face death. The loss of a friend, whether by death or departure overseas: the loss of a job, the loss of a much-loved home: these are everyday experiences of life, yet they are little deaths. When a son leaves home, when a daughter is married, when retirement comes, there is a dying to the old places and relationships to be accepted before we can discover new life: there is mourning to be done to set joy free. Even a man who loses a limb, his sight or hearing must do the proper work of mourning the loss of his capacity if he is to make possible a rebirth into the new life of a lame, blind or deaf man. Such losses will remind us sharply of the bodiliness of death: death is not just psychological.

On my return from West Africa I was constantly looking over my shoulder to the work and home I had left. Not until so many attachments to work and people in Africa had died out in me, was I set free for full commitment to life and work in this country, and incidentally to a new and less possessive love for Africa. This liberation is not achieved: it is given and received. We cannot command it: we can only do the things (such as mourning) which make the gift possible. The new life wells up from within. Life is trustworthy. We experience its power of renewal.

So those who learn to die in daily life find strangely familiar the last inevitable act of relinquishing all—self, life, body, friends, family, home and work; in hope that the promise of

70

life-through-death so faithfully honoured in life's little deaths, holds good for this death too.

John Taylor[95] writes:

> The fact of death exposes the nerve of that original fear, confronting man with ultimate impotence, abandonment, nothingness. So because he cannot assimilate it, it stays as the ever present enemy; because he cannot make it a way of life, it remains at the end of life. He has always known that 'in the midst of life we are in death', but in that knowledge death is dominant. . . . For the Christian this living with death is not merely an approaching end but a known pattern of experience. When he says 'In the midst of life we are in death', the dominant is 'life'. This is because he has taken the dying and rising of Jesus as the key to existence and has found that life-through-death is the authentic pattern of reality.

Not until we have accepted death and discovered life to be dominant over it, are we free to think and speak and act out of love for life and health, rather than attacking defects which are unconsciously feared as foretastes of physical death.

The following is a dialogue between a Zen Buddhist monk and his master:[96]

> 'What is the one ultimate word of truth?'
> 'Yes'
> 'I asked, what is the one ultimate word of truth?'
> 'I'm not deaf!'

The 'yes' to life and the future includes the 'yes' to biological death which comes to us as a gift with birth and life. This is the way we are. Each man dies that MAN may grow towards his evolutionary fulfilment. My individual biological death demands of me the complete gift of myself, all that I am and all that I have, to the future of the whole creation. That there is a future for MAN or a future life for myself is a matter of promise, hope and faith, but not proof.

In different ways the great religions have offered hope and promise for the future, in ways which have enabled men to live faithfully in the face of death. Belief in God has given men a sense of purposefulness in the creation and in their own lives by setting them free from belief in the ultimate power of death, and consequent meaninglessness.

In Europe widespread loss of Christian belief has resulted in a fear of death which has drained the word 'health' of its truly human dimension. Because our model of health is shaped by fear of biological death, cure of disease naturally becomes a supreme value: resources for the support and prolongation of life the supreme concern. To be able to say[97]

> There is no greater love than this, that a man should lay down his life for his friends,

a man must have found something greater to which to give his life than merely prolonging it.

In speaking of Sir Francis Chichester we used similar words. He found in the adventures and achievements of ocean sailing something worth the risk of his life. These 'greater things' for which men risk all, are sometimes a personal challenge; in peace or war men are caught up together in readiness to die for a friend, their family, tribe or country. But patriotism involves hatred. Edith Cavell (1914) said:

> Patriotism is not enough. I must have hatred for no man.

Her belief in God as the father of all men enabled her to see every man as a brother not as a rival, as one of us not one of them. She recognised hatred with its power to separate men from one another as a death to be feared more than the ending of her life. It is possible that this is in fact the death which we fear—the living death of hatred and bitterness, of war and de-humanisation—and that we displace this fear on to biological death.

My affirmation of another man—any other man—as my brother and not my rival demands of me (for completeness) a willingness to die that he may live. Death (true death, spiritual death, sin) is the pattern of behaviour which results from the denial of this. To become a Christian is not to be separated from other men, but to become aware of our unity with all creation and the family of MAN in a new way. It is to become willing to affirm as my brother and to give my life daily—even unto death—for any man be he/she young or old, healthy or sick, Christian or not, good, bad, white, mad, black, stranger or trusted friend. This is life and health, its denial is death. 'We

72

for our part have crossed over from death to life; this we know because we love our brothers'.[98]

Dag Hammarskjöld wrote:[99]

No choice is uninfluenced by the way in which the personality regards its destiny, and the body its death. In the last analysis, it is our conception of death which decides our answers to all the questions that life puts to us.

HEALTH AND MORALE

He had found something greater to do with his life than merely prolonging it (page 68).

The Abraham nature of man—man as the adventurer who left his home 'knowing not whither he went' to seek a more fully human way of life even at risk to himself and his companions (page 59).

Both these sentences imply that it may be safer to live at the 'chicken' level, rather than risk the greater possibilities of 'eaglehood' (see page 57). The man who leads his family, his party, his Church, his profession, or his nation into healthier styles of life brings them to the test. The risk of life and the risk of death are fellow journeymen. It is here that the idea of morale is a helpful one because it presents health in a different way.

I have referred previously (page 2) to the army method of classifying men as 'fit' for certain jobs. If a man has flat feet, then he may not be able to march far in full battle kit. But what he cannot do is of less importance than what he can do: the army is interested in his capability, for example, of driving and servicing vehicles. For this he is fit.

If the sickness rate of an army unit rises, it is the commanding officer—medically a layman—who has the responsibility for investigation and action. He will listen to the advice of his medical officer, but will also make a wider review of the situation as a whole. He will take into account all those factors which affect the morale of a unit. There are the basic hygiene requirements in terms of rations, facilities for drying clothes and boots, availability of married quarters, leave arrangements and rest periods. Obviously men's requirements vary much from a unit at home in peace-time, to a unit operating on foreign soil behind enemy lines in war-time.

There are also the factors which Hertzberg called motivators or Abraham needs. These are significant for the morale of an army unit. The nature of the task, especially, for which the unit exists, and the extent to which the unit understands and is committed to its task. The kind of leadership which the unit has, whether or not it trusts its officers. High morale in a unit will enable them to tolerate high levels of stress, including casualties and unfulfilled hygiene provision—such as wet clothes, lack of sleep, limited rations and water supplies. Every unit, however, like every individual, has its breaking-point.

During the Second World War in the North African campaign the malaria rate in an army unit was recognised as a matter of discipline. More than one commanding officer was demoted for a high malarial incidence in his unit. Good morale is reflected in low sickness and accident rates. The research work of Revans[100] among nurses and miners confirms this. A commanding officer faced with a rising sickness rate in his unit, will give first attention to the factors concerned with morale. He is working with a different idea of what constitutes a healthy unit and how you achieve health. If he worked to the medical idea of wellness he would ask for more doctors, more nurses and an extra wing for the sick bay!—a completely different approach to the nature of illness and health.

Two important points highlighted by the idea of morale are: firstly, that a healthy group of people can tolerate stress: that is, they are prepared to suffer. *Health does not exclude suffering.* Secondly, a group with high morale tolerates a deficiency of hygiene provision. (Scott's last expedition to the South Pole is a good example.) Is it possible to assess what *enough hygiene* would mean for an individual, a group or a people to achieve their task? These two points require further discussion.

(1) *Health includes suffering*

On page 27 we referred to the growing use of tranquillisers and other 'pills' to enable normal people to withstand stressful situations.

It is not possible to define 'normal' stress, because an individual's and a people's ability to withstand stress varies. It not only varies with temperament, with solitude or company, and with freshness or exhaustion, but also varies from time to time according to morale. We could describe an individual, a group or a people as having a high or low threshold for withstanding stress. In the United Kingdom the socially acceptable threshold appears to be diminishing. When stressed we turn more readily today than twenty years ago to the help of pills. It is arguable how far this is due to a greater availability of pills, their more ready prescription by doctors, the subtle persuasion of drug companies or low social morale.

The use of pills in this way meets our biological desire to escape from pain. It is part of our hygiene service. The distinction between use and misuse is difficult. We gave examples on page 27 of the differences of opinion with regard to the relief or withstanding of depression in bereavement, and of anxiety in a situation where funerals were delayed. If there is an examination to be taken, or we are nervous about a public ceremony do we muster courage or choose chemical control? Is some pain in childbirth normal? Or do we now expect a routine epidural anaesthetic? Have we answered these questions consciously and socially, or are we at the mercy of medical researchers and institutions whose assumptions about what is 'the done thing' sweep us passively along? Have we realised the ethical content in such choices, or let clinical facts dictate our answer?

Stress is a word used in engineering to describe the load which a given metal, girder or bridge can bear. In the same way stress on the human body is normal: the weight which certain bones and joints bear is the stimulus to muscle tone and growth as well as to the shaping of our skeleton. Similarly stress, in the sense of situations or feelings which cause us *distress*, is a universal experience. A person's growth towards maturity, therefore, includes a growing ability to withstand (i.e. stand with, as opposed to collapse under) the distresses of disappointment and pain, failure and depression, loss and bereavement.

We may describe certain people as the pain bearers of society. I am not here thinking of individuals or racial groups who become the scapegoats upon whom others project their hostility or guilt. That is not a healthy process because the wellness of some is at the involuntary cost of illness for others. I am thinking of those who voluntarily share the burdensome feelings of others. In a hospital, for example, which is an institution 'cradled in anxiety', ward sisters have to bear considerable stress from the projected feelings of other staff, patients and their families. This bearing can be creative for human relationships in a ward. Any position of responsibility or leadership in a family, a group or a nation carries with it the burden of making decisions and of bearing the consequences of one's own and other people's folly. The health of a family, a group, or a people depends upon the sharing of feelings of anxiety and guilt as well as joy and acceptance.

It is said that the Western way of life is particularly stressful today. This could be because either real causes of stress (such as speed and noise) have increased, or because our threshold of tolerance has diminished, or both. This could be met by resolution of the causes of stress (legislation about thresholds of noise), by the use of tranquillisers (from slot-machines in super-markets), by raising our threshold of tolerance through education (as in the training of army personnel and police, or at Outward Bound Schools), or by increase of morale (through political vision and action). To which of these ways priority is given will depend in part upon our concepts of health and how we become healthy. The choice carries long-term effects upon people that are difficult to assess.

John Macmurray wrote:[101]

> In imagination we feel sure that it would be lovely to live with a full and rich awareness of the world. But in practice sensitiveness hurts. It is not possible to develop the capacity to see beauty without developing also the capacity to see ugliness, for they are the same capacity. The capacity for joy is also the capacity for pain. We soon find that any increase in our sensitiveness to what is lovely in the world increases also our capacity for being hurt. This is the dilemma in which life has placed us.

A willingness to suffer is linked with human sensitivity and creativity. Much human art is born out of human travail.

Our way forward, if we wish to preserve both sensitivity and sanity is not through the abolition of stress, but in the development of group membership in which good morale and the sharing of feeling may increase the threshold to withstand stress together. The need for this is very evident today in hospitals.

Attitudes to suffering make a crucial difference between a model of health based upon the idea of morale and a medical model of health.

Few would deny that much human suffering is fearful and destructive. A passive resignation in the face of poverty and disease would undermine the great human endeavour to overcome those things which stunt human life. It is our very power to prevent suffering which now brings us to reconsider its place in human life, and to recognise stress as a potential builder as well as destroyer of human character. Adam flees from stress. Abraham counts the cost and presses onward. Each one of us is both Adam and Abraham.

Any Christian contribution to an understanding of what health is, would have to include suffering. Jesus himself, thought of as a model of humanness, 'the man', combined in his own actions the paradox of both relieving human suffering (he cured sick people); suffering himself (he deliberately set his face to go to Jerusalem); and bringing his friends into suffering (Peter denied him, Judas betrayed him, and the rest ran away).

Health positively includes suffering as a creative way of dealing with hostile and destructive feelings. The statement by a social worker in London (referring to teamwork between statutory and voluntary agencies) that:

> There is no problem we cannot solve if we will all work together,

is not only unrealistic but unhealthy; for 'man needs problems more than he needs solutions'.[102]

Lambourne wrote:[103]

> There could be no full health without sharing the burdens of sickness, so that a perfect health service where training, organisation and equipment totally removed the need for self-sacrifice is a logical impossibility.

That is a paradox at the heart of health. We work for health, but cannot attain it unless we are ready to risk its loss for the sake of one another.

(2) *Enough hygiene*

In our discussion above we suggested that an individual, a family, a group or a people whose morale is high can withstand a lack of hygiene provision. A low standard of living is tolerated by people either because they are apathetic (the effects of anaemia due to malaria and hookworm, for example), or because they are resigned to a seemingly inevitable situation in which they feel helpless (oppressed peasants, for example) or because their morale is high. In a fighting unit in the army enough hygiene and no more is provided: enough care and attention is given to basic biological necessities to enable the task to be completed.

How far is the idea of 'enough hygiene' of practical value in the management of a nation's resources? During the Second World War there was in the United Kingdom an overall plan to provide the population with the basic necessities to keep fit. Food grown at home and imported food, for example, were carefully calculated. There was 'enough' hygiene provided for the tasks in hand. Certain priority groups were established, e.g. pregnant mothers and children whose need for extra food was established. Firm leadership by Winston Churchill raised British morale to withstand shortages and stress. The concept of 'enough' hygiene has been established and has been proved workable. But motivation, so greatly dependent on leadership and morale, is the key to willingness to tolerate a lower standard of life (to suffer) for the sake of a worthwhile objective. There is, in other words, a context within which we are prepared to suffer, e.g. mountaineering, training for sport, helping others or a disaster situation.

The present context within which we have been describing the idea of 'enough' hygiene (page 73) is the understanding of our world as one world. It is a world in which the industrial countries grow rich and develop their 'health' care systems at the cost of exploiting other nations. The inequality is greatest between the Western nations and the third world. Indonesia can afford, for example, 1 franc per head per year for hygiene services: in Holland the sum available is 400 times as great. In Europe the infantile mortality rate has fallen to 17 per thousand, in the third world it is 300 or more per thousand.

The NHS in Britain does not remove all inequalities. Apart

from the possibility of private medical insurance through which privileges can be bought, it is in the generous allocation of money for one purpose and not another that most inequities arise. Reference has been made previously (page 10) to the support of intensive care units at the expense of less clinically rewarding spheres of care such as the after-care of those who are emotionally ill or handicapped.

Where there is such inequality, the question of a more just distribution of resources needs consideration.

What could be regarded as 'enough hygiene'? A level of hygiene facilities above which nations would not go until those below the level could catch up? A level of hygiene facilities above which a government would not give finance, until more basic facilities were available to all? Practical choices are always having to be made between one hygiene resource and another: between a new sheltered workshop for mentally handicapped people, or a kidney dialysis plant. This may be a difficult enough decision within a region where members of a Regional Health Authority have to make grave ethical decisions. To decide against a new renal dialysis unit will mean that some patients are going to die: to decide in favour of such a unit may mean death in another sense for other patients.

Only when we are prepared to let some people die will we be free to make more humane decisions in the distribution of hygiene resources. Our fear of death leads us to use death as the final incontrovertible argument. We are prepared to tolerate much human misery, overcrowding and meaninglessness in order to save a few lives. We tolerate death in the quality of life on a large scale in order to prolong a few lives biologically.

Men have not yet been sufficiently moved by a sense of justice to share resources on the required scale between nations. Here lie the seeds of war. Redistribution of resources appears unlikely without a bitter struggle for redistribution of power. Through organisations like the World Health Organisation, the Christian Medical Commission of the World Council of Churches, and relief organisations like Oxfam, Inter-church Aid and Intercare men are working internationally to bring hygiene where it is needed. But charity is insufficient, we require just men to lead the nations into greater responsibility for one another.

Enough hygiene still does not guarantee health, although a

willingness to share resources would in itself be a sign of health. We speak of 'underdeveloped' countries, by which we mean nations which have not achieved industrial development leading to wealth, wellness and longevity. But the word under-development tells us little about the health and quality of life in those societies. African rural societies are notorious for the weight of illness, parasitic infections and malnutrition which they suffer. But they are also justly famous for the richness of their celebrations in song and dance amid poverty: they are also famous for their hospitality. The word 'richness' is open to interpretation in two ways: lavish celebrations (by hygiene standards) are not always humanly enriching (by health standards).

The Office of Health Economics has published a study[104] which draws attention to the difference between our demands in regard to the NHS and what in fact we require. Our demands are continually rising: for example we used to regard blindness, deafness and absence of teeth as fairly usual in old age, but now we expect relief. There is in fact almost no limit to our rising demands. In Africa expectations are much lower.

We (both patients and doctors) are also unwilling to admit that there are many treatments given for conditions for which we can in fact do little or nothing. We are squandering limited resources on treatment that has not been scientifically evaluated. In part this is because doctors often have not got the time to listen, to understand and to make relationships with their patients. We prescribe things instead.

Health is the milieu (human and environmental) which enables people individually and socially to grow towards full-ness of life. This is one description (among many) which we have made. To use the word 'towards' reminds us that men look forward to an ideal. For the ideal person and society we may speak of 'wholeness'—that which 'awaits the day when sorrow and sighing shall cease and death shall be no more'. That day is not yet. In the present we continually fall short of wholeness. We suffer from loss of vision. But a vision of fullness of human life is essential to inspire us to build a healthy society now in a world where men are sick and resources are limited.

We need to discover an economic concept of 'Enough',[105] which is thought out as thoroughly as was the provision of hygiene in the United Kingdom during the Second World War.

But any limitation of medical and hospital services will only be tolerated if a high degree of social morale is inspired in people. We need a complete reorientation in our ways of thinking about health, for today we are set upon a course of achieving health which not only does not lead to health, but which is also inevitably costing more and more.

Perhaps health like happiness is a surprising gift, not just an achievement.

GOOD AND EVIL

There are different assumptions about good and evil in what we have written about health. We have described a concept of health closely related to a people's culture and to the way in which they see 'the good life' and strive to obtain it. Implicit in such a vision is an attitude towards what is seen to be bad and harmful, and how to prevent, avoid, change or destroy it.

Beliefs about good and evil in Western culture are widely related to the Christian tradition. Lambourne[106] has described how the Church's concept of sin and Medicine's concept of disease have influenced one another. Even today doctors and clergy have more in common in their attitudes to 'goodness' and 'badness' than either suppose. Medicine and Church are mirror images of one another. Both have among their founders men who held an unbalanced view of salvation and pastoral practice. This lack of balance afflicted all Christian thought, though it reached its worst expression in certain decadent forms of protestantism.

Its exponents, influenced by a rampant individualism and morbidness, defined salvation and health as the end points of a process in which individuals and their professional deliverers (doctors and clergy) concentrated on their badness (sin, disease, poverty) until all were eliminated. Goodness (salvation, health, richness) need then be given scant attention since it is a by-product of the concentration on eliminating the badness. Badness in this scheme of salvation and pastoral practice then becomes more real for its practitioners than goodness; pathology more real than health; and whilst disease is closely scrutinised and dominates the consciousness of the observer, the patient in his healthiness and in his

81

healthy relation with other persons is only on the periphery of awareness. Thus subtly does salvation (health) come to be defined by sins (diseases)! Thus we see how Church and Medicine can reinforce each others' distorted and inadequate understanding of good and evil.

In the Old Testament[107] a ceremony is described in which the sins of the people were ritually put on to a scapegoat which was driven out into the wilderness. The whole tribe must be purified. Cleansing was obtained by separation from the 'bad'. In other cases the individual was either excommunicated from the community, put to death or exorcised. In these ways evil was believed to be removed from the community.

When people deal with evil in this way they are understanding it as something external to themselves which invades their personal and social life in a disruptive way. In Western culture we have developed a system of medicine based upon a perception of illness as a pattern of violence:[108]

> Advertisements for life insurance remind us that the family breadwinner may suddenly be crippled or killed by a coronary thrombosis. An epidemic of flu may, overnight, disrupt a city's bus service. Accident, infection, degeneration, nervous breakdown, may violate a man, his freedom, his capacity to work, his ambitions, or his family. Like the sinner, the sick man is a victim not a villain. . . . In the face of this alien power we have matched violence with counter-violence. We have developed potent drugs, skilled techniques of surgery. . . . The conquest of disease is one of our great human achievements—the very word conquest suggests the violence of this struggle. Eradication (say, of malaria), abortion, electro-convulsive therapy, transplants—our healing vocabulary points to the violence, the breaking in of power and counterpower from outside, as it were.

There is at the same time another quite different attitude to 'badness' implicit in what we have written about health. We have denied that illness is always bad. It may be a learning experience, a source of readaptation for an individual or a family to their life situation. It may be the foreseen cost of a great human endeavour, or the unforeseen penalty of folly. It may be a warning voice that a particular habit or life-style is harmful. Illness *may* be a good. We have suggested (page 74) that suffering is included in the concept of health.

It is not in fact possible to eradicate evil in the ways implicit in the medical model. Scapegoats may be driven into the desert, but sooner or later men learn to irrigate the desert and live in it, and they find that there is no further desert into which the scapegoats may be chased away. Sooner or later we or our children have to learn to live with the consequences of our folly. Health is inclusive. The groups upon whom we project our fears and hatred such as the 'Niggers-Made in Whiteman's land' (page 67) lay claim to our brotherhood. We must take back our fears and hatred and bear them ourselves.

Patriotism is not enough: I must have hatred for no man.

This way towards health, which assumes that badness is not something which can be externalised and projected, is powerfully presented in the crucifixion and resurrection of Jesus. The cross is the model of a different way of dealing with evil, of bearing it. On the cross Christ suffered the hatred and brutality of his enemies and his friends, withstood it, and gave back forgiveness to those who nailed his hands, understanding to the thieves at his side, and love to his mother and John. It is this way towards health through suffering which is denied in Western culture today.

Those who think and act in accordance with these different schemata perceive 'badness' in different ways, and accordingly seek different ways towards the good life. It is different attitudes like this which mould a people's ideas of health and direct their search towards it.

I have described two different beliefs about how to deal with 'badness'—eradication and suffering—both of which need to exist in harmony in our Western culture. I am not proposing that we should 'suffer' malnutrition or cancer. This would betray the human endeavour to relieve destructive suffering. But I am equally *not* proposing that we should try to eradicate all stress or suffering as 'bad'. They can be sources of strength and health. I have written elsewhere[109] of the hard practical decisions which this means for everyone who suffers or helps sufferers.

Today it is doctors and social workers, trained in biological, behavioural and social sciences, who are influencing profoundly our ideas about what it means to be human, and how to achieve health. We may speak of a 'clinicalisation'[110] of twentieth-century urban culture. In many parts of the world this clinical model has affected the style of ministry in the Church. Clinical pastoral counselling, closely modelled on medical and social-work practice, is replacing pastoral theology.

It would be foolish to pretend that I have fully discussed the problem of evil and suffering with which so many men down the ages have wrestled. I have simply pointed to the decisive influence of a people's beliefs about good and evil, in the formation of their concept of health and of the way they set out to achieve it. Such beliefs, often unexamined but tenaciously held, have far-reaching consequences in terms of health care and social services, professional training and design of buildings.

PART IV

Towards Health—an Exploration

The descriptions of health which we have made (see summary on pages 107–116) have practical implications for the NHS in Britain. Our beliefs about the nature of health and how we develop towards a healthy society, affect the design of buildings, the style and training of professions and the order of priorities for the allocation of resources, both money and manpower. Beliefs have expensive consequences.

THE SOCIAL CONTEXT OF THE NHS

We must not mistake medical treatment for health care.[III]

In discussing the influence of public health and psychiatry on our concepts of health (pages 43–45) we described some of the areas of personal and social life to which we must refer when we try to describe or measure health. One of these areas (among many) is the NHS whose function is to make and keep us well (diagram 6). This is one service among a whole constellation of hygiene services (diagram 7) necessary for our biological or creaturely welfare. Hygiene, in its turn, is one factor which, interrelated with 'Abraham' factors, forms the milieu in which personal and social health may grow (diagram 8). The three diagrams together (diagram 9) represent the context of the NHS.

The NHS in the left-hand box (diag. 6) is contained within the middle box (diag. 7) as one among many hygiene factors. The middle box (diag. 7) is contained within the right-hand

85

box (diag. 8) as a constellation of hygiene factors interacting (shown by dotted line enclosure) with various Abraham factors to make health possible.

Taking the three boxes (diagrams 6, 7 and 8) as a whole (diag. 9) the context widens as we move from left to right; and narrows as we move from right to left. Towards the left we focus upon illness: towards the right we move towards health. Towards the left we are analysing and breaking down wholes into smaller parts. Towards the right we are bringing parts together and building them into greater wholes.

Health cannot be understood by analysis, but only through a kind of building process. Health is like a married couple. The marriage of a man and a woman enhances their individuality, and also introduces a new element of unity into the relationship. One and one makes three not two. In building the greater whole—a marriage—a surprise element appears over and above the simple sum of the parts—a man and a woman.

Likewise in analysing interpersonal concepts such as 'empathy', we lose something when we try to break it down into its component parts (identification, suffering, understanding, warmth). We can go further and break down each component into smaller components but already the meaning of the whole is lost. It may become a game people play.

Health is understood by bringing parts together. In diagram 8 the hygiene factors are depicted in an open box to show that the Abraham factors are distinct but not separate. Responsibility, for example, may be given to or withheld from a patient in hospital, denying or enabling the possibility of a healthy response to illness. Pupils in a sixth form, or students in a university may or may not be given an opportunity to share in the shaping of their course, denying or giving them an opportunity for healthy growth towards maturity. Health is always that further possibility in human life to which experience, encouragement or friendship may point. Health makes sense of the work of the NHS and other hygiene factors such as education, agriculture and housing. Health is the wider context within which medicine, teaching and politics are practised.

Only in its wider context can medicine be properly valued and not overvalued. This could lead to the withdrawal of medical domination from inappropriate areas. For example,

86

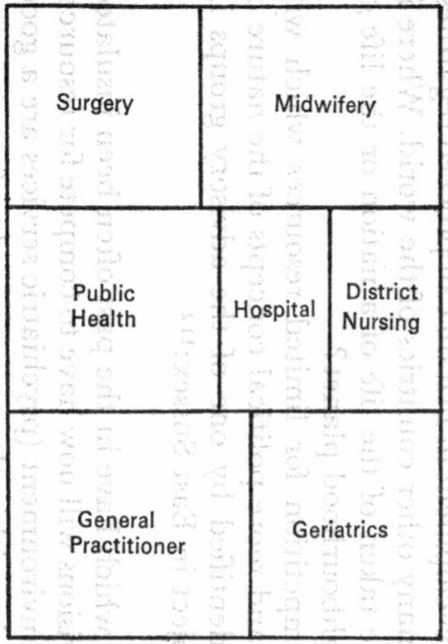

Diagram 6. NHS

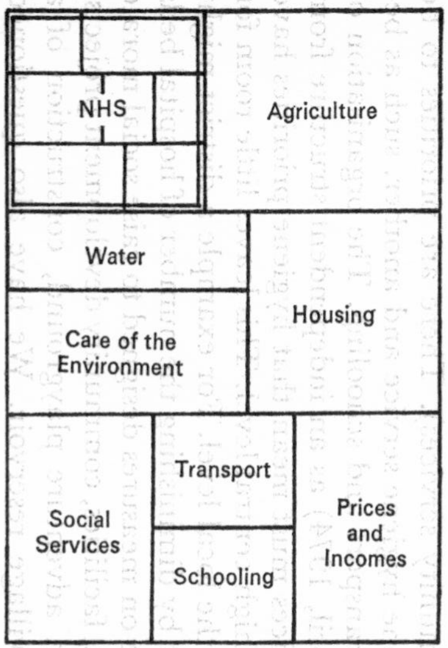

Surgery · Midwifery · District Nursing · Public Health · Hospital · Geriatrics · General Practitioner · NHS

Diagram 7. Hygiene

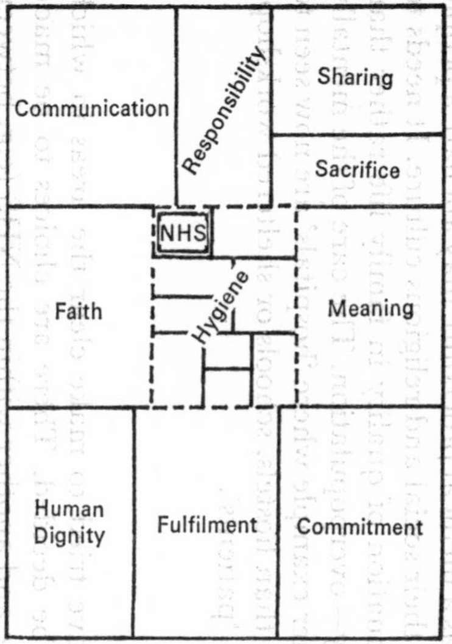

Agriculture · Housing · Prices and Incomes · Transport · Water · Schooling · NHS · Care of the Environment · Social Services

Diagram 8. Health

Sharing · Sacrifice · Meaning · Communication · Responsibility · Commitment · NHS · Hygiene · Faith · Fulfilment · Human Dignity

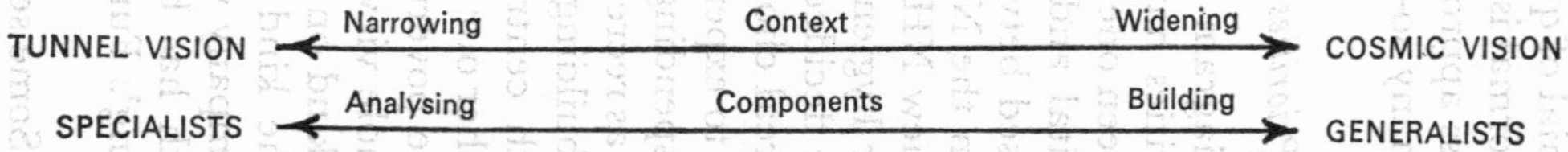

Diagram 9. The Context of the NHS

TUNNEL VISION ←→ COSMIC VISION
SPECIALISTS ←→ GENERALISTS

Narrowing · Analysing · Context · Components · Building · Widening

Handwritten marginal notes:

Also rsk have right rel'nship with self, other + whole environment.

rel. is only a part, but a new part.

Salvation, as does even health = right rel'nship with God (see axioms → page) made poss. by wk of C

C is a
C = subset of

Christianity ⊂ Religion ⊂ Faith ⊂ Health

can be divided as can NHS diag 6 — catholicism, charismatic, methodists etc — all have part of the whole picture.

" can not be all + end all, but a part of the whole.

Rel. is not the be all + end all, but a part of the whole.

there is no reason why people should have to be treated as patients in a family planning service: indeed the presentation of family planning as a medical procedure may alienate a people and do violence to their social and religious culture. It needs to be seen as an affirmation of quality in family life rather than a denial of quantity—overpopulation. The care of the mentally subnormal is another example where 'hospitals' are now seen to be less appropriate than hostels, schools or sheltered workshops for many so-called 'patients'.

(1) *Priorities*

In diagram 9 I have tried to make clear the areas in which priorities have to be decided. There are choices to be made between one service and another within the NHS (e.g. between hospital and community services). There are priorities to be assessed between one hygiene service and another, such as between the NHS, transport and schooling. The organisation of the new NHS (April, 1974) as an independent structure from other hygiene services must mean that hygiene priorities have to be decided at a high central level. This leaves little room for any real choice at the local level. For example a district might wish to experiment by diminishing the number of hospital beds and spending more on measures designed to raise social morale such as recreational facilities, community development projects, the building of an adventure playground, construction of a health centre or village reservoir. We have also questioned whether our own development in Britain can proceed regardless of the poverty in many other countries of the world. Where is a whole view to be taken of the life of a nation or the life of mankind on a neighbourhood planet?

The kind of competition for limited resources which will accompany wider and more political concepts of the nature of health has been identified by one of the advisory groups in a King's Fund project in East Sussex:[112]

Some services which have in the past often been insulated by structural divisions will now have to compete for resources in a more fluid environment (psychiatric services are a good example). Likewise within the same area, local government projects or services directly relevant to health, like home

helps or sheltered housing, will have to compete with resources for other projects or services, like libraries or swimming pools.

For lack of a whole view our priorities in research too often
depend upon the sensitivity or enthusiasm of individuals or
groups who become concerned about one particular problem.

Bryant[113] has suggested certain criteria for assessing *medical*
priorities. His simple method is used by medical and nursing
students working in rural Thailand. Four criteria are used:

Prevalence, which refers to the frequency with which the problem
  occurs;
Seriousness, that is the destructiveness of the problem for individuals and society;
Community Concern, which includes the knowledge, attitudes and
  feelings of urgency about a problem; and
Vulnerability to Management, which takes into account the availability of methods of managing the problem as well as the costs
  and effectiveness of applying them.

The inclusion of *community concern* is important because it is
through information and education that public concern may
become more realistic, and the community more knowledge-
able and responsible in the decisions that it takes for its health.
For example, we have described in Part I some of the things
which arouse excessive concern such as death and drug dependence. There are other things about which we are comparatively unconcerned; for example, the lack of education of
our feeling life, living conditions of the elderly and handicapped, growing prejudice against coloured immigrants, the
lingering stigma of mental illness and the widespread use of
tranquillisers. The importance of the NHS as an information
service for the nation is evident.

To list certain general concerns of this kind may tempt us to
shape them as problems to be solved. But they are symptoms of
social attitudes, and an indirect solution may have to be sought
through changes in society's beliefs and values. In the re-
organisation of the NHS (April, 1974) we have created Community Health Councils who hold a key to this third way that
Bryant uses for assessment of priorities—community concern.

It is essential that these lay councils see their role as concerned with the promotion of health and not the eradication of illness. We have made an important distinction between hygiene and health (diagram 9). What is commonly referred to as Comprehensive *Health* Planning[114] is primarily concerned with the provision of *hygiene*, with meeting man's biological requirements—his Adam needs. It is important to give proper attention to such basic essentials for living. But health relates to further human possibilities (man's Abraham needs) for responsibility, sharing in local political decisions, communication, celebration and interpersonal relationships. It is equally important to give proper attention to these further factors which have an important influence on social morale and which may make quality of life possible.

In any discussion or conference on *health*, truth is best served by a wide representation of civil interests, which might include people such as teachers, artists, miners, housewives, politicians, immigrants, architects, civil engineers, civil servants, midwives and environmentalists. These are people who are not primarily interested in the symptoms of what is going wrong in society. Similarly representatives of voluntary bodies also need to come from a wide span of healthy interests, such as sport, drama and youth organisations, not just those concerned with sickness and crises. Doctors are authoritative on the subject of illness, but in matters of health carry the same authority as, for example, teachers, mothers and environmentalists. Doctors and other professions in the NHS and Social Services will continue to contribute significantly to the comprehensive planning of hygiene services: but their contribution is *one* contribution among many, and the NHS is one institution among many (diagram 7).

It is the members of a society who must say what they mean by health (there are no health specialists) and must make the ethical and political choices involved. Words like 'needs' and 'priorities' appear to be objective descriptions of facts and processes but they conceal value judgements.[115]

Community Health Councils are one of the possible agents of change in social thinking. They have access to information and to the media, for communicating their ideas. Their annual report is public. At present, however, in England, a Community Health Council (of 18–30 members) 'represents' a population of 100,000 to 450,000. The word 'represent' is deliberately put in inverted commas because it is not possible for anyone to represent effectively a larger grouping than about 500–1,000 people.[116] The Councils however are empowered to appoint sub-groups, and in this way could achieve local participation. We might then recover a sense that the NHS is 'ours', that the hospitals are 'ours' and that ordinary people can play their part in building a healthy society.

Discussion between doctors and laity as equals is essential. The authority of doctors, proper to their own field, is inappropriate if carried over into discussions on health. This is one of the most far-reaching changes which an abandonment of the medical model of health would bring in society. We have referred to the kinds of change required in professional roles (page 53) and doctors already involved in such radical re-orientation of their outlook have described what this has meant for the style of their professional work. Members of Community Health Councils will have to win the confidence of professions working in the NHS, knowing that change is costly. We might prefer to think of such changes as Utopian. But we cannot. *They are already taking place.* Many doctors and nurses are responding with courage to the kinds of changes which we have described in Part II.

An important part of the Community Health Councils' time should be given to thinking out ways of raising public morale, because we have seen how closely the ideas of morale and mental health are related. This is an indirect way of dealing with many of the ills to which their attention is sure to be drawn. Only if they continue to see themselves as partly responsible for the whole (health), not wholly responsible for a part (NHS), will they remain a Community *Health* Council, for they will be under constant pressure to talk about illness. The following is from an editorial in *Community Medicine*:[117]

Others look wider, seeking to determine the relationship between that service and a wide range of other considerations which are relevant to the health and well-being of the community, including the personal social services, education, environmental control, housing and occupational matters.

91

The wider approach is necessary, as health services cannot be considered in isolation from the rest of our social fabric and institutions, and attempts to plan and develop these services *in vacuo* will lead to failure.

INSTITUTIONS

(1) *Health centres*

Beliefs shape buildings: and buildings shape beliefs. One of the best examples of this in recent years was the Peckham Experiment.[118] The Peckham Health Centre contained a cafeteria, a large hall, swimming bath, infant nurseries and a beginner's swimming bath, gymnasium, theatre, and an outside hard area where roller-skating, etc. could be played. It was a centre for family, not individual, membership. There was a research laboratory where observations were made (the whole centre being an experiment for the study of human biology) and where individual and family consultations were held. The medical laboratory visibly subserved the main purpose of the Centre which was health. The Centre provided equipment and facilities in a poor area of London for the development of its members' gifts and for the enlargement of their hearts and minds. One of its intentions is well illustrated by the following:[119]

> Quite spontaneously they (young couples) have come some months beforehand asking, for instance, that their periodic health overhaul might be put forward because they were expecting to go on holiday at such and such a date, and hoped to start their first baby then. They wanted to know that they were as fit as they could be when conception occurred. . . . There are young families who before joining the centre had determined never to have any, or any more children, but who after being members for a year or two also seek a consultation to tell us that they now intend to have a baby. They have changed their minds owing to their fuller and different understanding of the meaning of pregnancy and the ease and success with which they see it accomplished by members of the centre. These actual happenings pointed to a changed outlook . . .

I am not suggesting we copy the Peckham model: we are in any case a different people to what we were thirty years ago and attitudes are different. But the Peckham model illustrates three things:

(i) An assumption about the many-sided nature of health and its positive quality is in-built. It reminds us painfully, today, of how fragmented we have become.

(ii) Healthy people are not *primarily* concerned with doctors and nurses but with family relationships, swimming baths, roller-skating and dramatics. The professionals who are concerned for the families' health make 'good enough' individual and social life possible. They help the families to make full use of the Centre's facilities.

(iii) The power of such an institution to produce 'changed outlook'. Hospitals (and Health Centres) powerfully and insidiously mould people's attitudes to life, death and technology.

The modern Health Centres are polyclinics shaped by the belief that we achieve health by the prevention, diagnosis and treatment of disease. The buildings shape the beliefs of those who grow up with them and the language of illness becomes their language, until it can actually be difficult, as in Britain today, to speak of health in any other way.

The Peckham Health Centre and the Health Centres of the 1970s are built on different beliefs about what health is and how you work towards it.

Two general practitioners in Birmingham[120] collected information from their patients about what kind of Health Centre they would wish to see built. By no means everyone wished for a polyclinic. There were suggestions such as the provision of a coffee bar which hinted at a desire for something more convivial: and a wish for health education. We need to evolve alternative designs for health centres which take notice of the opinions of local consumers.

(2) *Hospitals*

A hospital has been described as a 'living learning arena'.[121] This description points to the fact that in a hospital the staff as well as patients and their families are constantly faced by crises. The experiences of illness, handicap or bereavement are some of the most tragic crises which a man may meet. The success of a difficult operation, having a baby, or a new discovery by a research worker are some of the most triumphant crises which a woman may meet. Being human and not robots we are changed by such situations for better or for worse. A crisis is an opportunity: by the way we respond to it and learn from it we are made stronger or weaker. Such lessons of life are seldom individual, usually shared, and are not confined to the hospital in the same way, for example, as major surgery is. On their return home, patients share their experiences of hospital life with their families, neighbours and colleagues. Such experiences mould public opinion and as a result of them our family and friends are more or less ready to consult their doctors in future: more or less ready to vote for resources to be allocated to motorways or hospitals: more or less ready to bring up their children with or without prejudices about health, nursing as a career or the status of doctors in society: more or less afraid of death.

Hospitals, in fact, are a school of life. Lambourne[122] has described them as important socialising agencies. In Part I, I described some of the beliefs, attitudes and assumptions upon which hospital medicine is based (pages 8–32). These beliefs, attitudes and assumptions are conveyed powerfully to patients just because they are assumed and not thought about. One of the lessons learnt in hospital is the nature of 'health'. I have suggested elsewhere[123] that this is the most significant task which a hospital performs in society. The primary task of the hospital can be described as:

> To enable patients, their families and staff to learn from the experience of illness and death how to build a healthy society.

However, in hospital—particularly teaching hospitals—the medical model of health is powerfully operant, conditioning men's attitudes and beliefs. We must take seriously this influence of the hospital as a living learning arena, for today it is working against health. The research of King, Raynes and Tizard[124] to which we have already referred (page 11), showed that nurses trained in hospital act differently and have quite different attitudes towards mentally handicapped children when compared with social workers trained in residential care. Nurses are

94

trained in hospitals dominated by medical attitudes: social workers are not.

Community hospitals promise a new pattern of treatment and aftercare. We have already referred to the continuing care unit initiated in a community hospital (the Thayer hospital).[125] One of the basic differences in this unit is the way in which staff understand health and disease in terms of man's adaptation to his environment. This shifts the whole emphasis of their work from disease to people. The model of health underlying the work is a functional one, and the style of medicine to which this gives rise is different. For example, there is a striking continuity about life in hospital and life at home after discharge. The persistence of illness or handicap is treated as a situation in which patients, their families and staff together think out not only a régime of treatment but also a mode of life.

The patient's strengths rather than weaknesses have become the object of interest. He is helped to be as fully a person, as fully alive, as his limitations permit. This is the same kind of human victory which some hospices for the dying[126] achieve. Illness, even terminal illness, is a part of life to be lived. The word 'care', emphasised by the adjective 'continuing', means the maintenance of human personality as something of value in itself. The continuing care unit has deliberately set its face against becoming just another specialised unit. Its aim is to help all physicians to give continuing care.

In such a unit the nurse gains in responsibility and status. Nursing is seen to be a profession in its own right, not simply a paramedical profession: it is as true to say that medicine is a paranursing profession.

The continuing care unit is consciously used as a 'living learning arena' in which education is important. Matters of individual and family morale are given attention. Health is understood more in terms of the response or adaptation of individuals and their families to a particular situation. Much thought is given to ways in which a person's capacity for active life can be maximised, and his disability overcome. This style of medical and nursing care was bound to be reborn in a unit where cure of disease could not be the supreme value because people were suffering from incurable illness or were dying. It is a style of medical practice which is situational, that is, it is properly related to the pattern of illness and the needs of people

95

in the area in which it is set. This stands in contradistinction to our present style of medicine in the United Kingdom in which the interests of those who supply the service may dominate those of the consumers.

(3) *Buildings*

In the context of social health we need to think how the concept of inclusiveness (page 67) could affect buildings. The design of hospital buildings too often makes an artificial separation from the community. In psychiatric, geriatric and mentally subnormal hospitals it should be possible to design certain facilities on the periphery such as shops or canteens which were open both to patients and the public. Small hostels could also be built on the periphery which had access to both hospital and community, and which matched the designs of local housing. Hospitals are part of the community.

FROM ILLNESS TO HEALTH

(1) *On going sick healthily*

One of the factors in health which we have mentioned is the sense of responsibility (diagram 8, page 87). We have discussed how the very word 'patient' may suggest abrogation of responsibility, and the gift of supreme authority to the doctor. It is at the point where an illness is relatively unshaped either by doctor or patient that the patient may be encouraged to respond healthily to sickness.

Going sick is a complex process. Balint[127] has explored the patient/doctor relationship with a group of general practitioners over a long period of time. They found that patient and doctor may shape the nature of the illness between them. The patient offers certain symptoms which the doctor may accept or reject. The doctor expresses more interest in one direction than another, and the patient may agree or refuse to follow. The relationship is like a dance.

Doctors may therefore collude with a patient's desire to be ill. The patient may mislead his doctor or refuse to acknowledge that the doctor is right (perhaps) in asking him personal questions about his style of life. Patient, or doctor, or both may refuse relationship. There are, in fact, on the side of both doctor and patient healthy and unhealthy ways to respond to the illness. The doctor's and the patient's interests are not necessarily the same.

Hardie[128] writes:

> Consumers tend to give first priority to the accessibility of good primary care. Providers (especially within the medical profession) are tending to concentrate on the technically complex and interesting.

But it is now becoming clear that the distinction between being 'ill' and 'well' is not always as simple as it appears. Many surveys have shown[129] that exactly the same kinds of disease, defects and pathology are found in people who do not seek medical help, as among those who do 'go sick'. By 'going sick' I mean that a person accepts that he is sick, seeks help from someone and consents to being treated as ill. I. K. Zola[130] has conducted research into the reasons why some people having a particular trouble 'go sick' and why others—with the same trouble—do not 'go sick'. He found differences of attitude to 'going sick' between races. He also found that several factors influenced people in seeking help, such as the effect of some complaint on their ability to work, or its beginning in some way to disturb their personal or family relationships. He found also that social relationships influence our going sick or not: we may unconsciously look for social permission or approval before opting for the role of 'sick person'.

Perhaps the most important of Zola's findings is that unless a doctor not only pays attention to the pathology, but also to the reason why the sick man 'went sick' when he did, the patient is not so likely to persevere with treatment: that is, the healer does not get a chance to practise his art.

In Great Britain it is often assumed that the general medical practitioner is the primary assessor of illness. In fact the first assessor of illness is the patient. The patient himself, to begin with, may see certain signs such as a swelling or skin rash; or have certain feelings such as pain, which lead him to consult someone else. With experience we get much better at knowing what pains to ignore (stiffness after unaccustomed exercise), what simple remedies to prescribe for ourselves (a Disprin for a headache after a hot day's shopping, or a lotion from the chemist for nits in the children's hair) and for what conditions to seek further help (loss of weight for which I cannot account). To varying degrees we consult our husbands or wives and members of the family, neighbours or colleagues at work. Mothers of families have to be skilled primary assessors of trouble and illness.

In Africa the family consultation is very important and may lead to a decision whether to go to hospital or not. Certain diseases like epilepsy are thought to be beyond the skill of a Western doctor. Other diseases like Yaws are known to respond dramatically to his hypodermic injection.

Sufferers may rightly or wrongly come to the conclusion that some diseases are not the province of a doctor but that a social worker, marriage guidance counsellor, osteopath, faith healer or the retired nurse next door could give better help. One professional whose advice is often sought is the pharmacist. Two studies (in Chester[131] and South London[132]) have been made, and details of the kind of advice asked from pharmacists have also been published.[133]

In Part II (page 45) I described the increasing extent to which people in distress look for personal help outside the realm of traditional medicine. Older people have been found[134] more likely to take some worry to their local minister; but although it is often now said that the general practitioner hears the confessions that the priest once heard, in fact few general practitioners devote time to counselling people with personal problems. Dr. Field[135] records that at the forest shrines in Ashanti the priest sees very large numbers of sick and troubled people. We have already referred (page 41) to the development of 'bare foot doctors', feldshers or medical assistants in Africa, India and China. In Britain the work of the practice nurses is in many ways comparable (page 41).

At one of the large city-centre churches in London, St. Martin-in-the-Fields, the whole process of human beings seeking out one another when in distress reaches an almost archetypal level. Some men have been through the whole range of helping organisations, statutory and voluntary, as well as compulsory orders to psychiatric hospital and prison. It is often not clear why one man goes to prison and another to psychiatric hospital: nor is it clear why one person can help someone when others have failed. The pattern of human distress gets shaped by those who try to help. A problem may so harden that no progress is possible until someone sees the distressed person in a different frame of reference, as an ordinary person, perhaps, with whom you share a meal. It sometimes helps someone to direct their attention away from their problem to more positive areas of themselves and their life. Personal relationship can sometimes set people free from the bonds that diagnosis and treatment have tied around them: can create a new identity for them by affirming their strengths, rather than denying their weaknesses. It is often not a matter of whether a man is sick or sinful, but of *who can give him a healing experience*.

There are many people, lay and professional, who are first involved in assessing, responding to, and shaping the first signs and symptoms of trouble. The purpose of describing some of the complex ways in which illness/problems present is to put the work of the general practitioner in perspective. He is not in fact a *primary* assessor: patients turn to the general medical practitioner for a variety of reasons, medical, social and financial.[136] A doctor (as now trained) may be too specialised to be a primary assessor, and one of his roles must be to educate and support those people—lay and professional—whose help is sought initially by sick people.

Basic to any NHS, therefore, is the training of a population in how to use the general practitioner and social services. Not only is it desirable to increase people's understanding of wellness and illness but to give people more responsibility for their own self-care and neighbourly care. We are *both* patients and agents in our own recovery.

In Western society the general practitioner is at present a general *medical* practitioner. Is a medical training in fact the most suitable for a general practitioner? If now in Western society there is so much emotional and behavioural illness, might not a casework training be more useful with some secondary knowledge of medicine? A general practitioner primarily trained in casework would score heavily in sorting out human and social problems, but might miss the occasional acute appendicitis. His/her view of people and life would be wider than that of a hospital-trained practitioner—more ecological in outlook. Common to both a medically trained and a casework trained general practitioner is the clinical method.

This is the ability to view the patient/client objectively and to make a diagnosis or assessment of him and his disease in relationship to family and environment. Practitioners trained in casework, however—social workers—are more aware of the risks of dependence and speak of 'client self-determination' more than doctors: their whole approach is much less manipulative.

Another type of professional training which has been considered suitable for an early assessor of disease is nursing. J. R. Ellis[137] has argued cogently for the use of the 'practice nurse', and useful experience is now accumulating from various experiments.[138] Many patients are content to consult a nurse in the same way that they consult a pharmacist. The image of the nurse as one who cares, makes her a more approachable person. She is much more 'one of us' than the doctor whose professional style makes him a bit remote. She is often more feminine and motherly and appeals to that side of our nature which is seeking nurture (nursing). I deliberately write feminine, for it is possible for a woman to assume the basically masculine outlook of a doctor and to forfeit her nurturing role. (I have written elsewhere[139] of the violent nature of illness and the counter-violence of much scientific medicine.)

The District Nurse is already an acceptable visitor to homes of sickness. The Health Visitor (also a nurse) is almost unique in being able to visit homes where there is no crisis or illness: her commonest duty being concerned with small children and the hygiene education of mothers. The authority of these community nurses is an acceptable blend of skill and homeliness.

A general practitioner, therefore, requires a basic training in family care rather than hospital medicine. This would require far more emphasis in his/her training on the study of human growth and development, group dynamics and casework. Much of family care however is intuitive and difficult to teach. The range of gifts, knowledge and skills required for general practice may be beyond the competence of one person to acquire in a reasonable period of study.

In which case the general practitioner will need to be a troika: a nurse, a doctor and a social worker. Each of the three professions has something to contribute to a greater whole—general practice. This is not simply a teamwork model, with an assumption that the doctor is the leader of the team. Their relationship may be worked out in new ways appropriate to the situation in the way Morley (page 40) has worked out a new nurse/doctor relationship in his under-fives clinics. This means a new style of being a doctor, a nurse, a social worker.

(2) *Health promotion*

Apart from the Health Visitor, the professions mentioned in the last section are primarily concerned with illness and wellness. But health may appear in or through illness and suffering. Illness may be a learning experience. A leper settlement may be a healthy community. A hospital ward may likewise be healthy or sick. The possibility of health in these situations depends upon people, professional or lay, who promote the further possibility of health. Nurses, doctors or patients may be creators or destroyers of health among themselves or others. The health of a ward may stem from the influence of a patient, a nurse or a domestic cleaner.

In the community at large there are key people who promote health or illness. Caplan[140] has written of the importance of police, midwives, teachers, barmen, bus-conductors, the man or woman who runs the corner shop or bingo hall, the grannie in a street, and the mother of a family. Every community has its key people who listen to, advise and help their neighbours, colleagues or chance acquaintances. They are the kind of people to whom others turn in a crisis. They are the carriers of a society's culture and therefore the actual builders or destroyers of health. They are key people in any attempt to change a society's attitudes or values in relation to health, illness, life and death. They can be the salt that brings out the flavour of a people's life together, if the salt has not lost its savour.

PART V CONCLUSION

Summary of Practical Implications

1. We need *to reshape our beliefs* about health and our understanding about illness. The reformation of beliefs and attitudes is basic to all other practical suggestions.

In particular the clinical model of health, based upon a search for health by the eradication of disease, is leading to greater knowledge of disease and more and more costly ventures to prevent or treat it. We as people need once again to be able to choose a style of health which can enhance our humanness both individual and social.

2. Those who work in the Health Care Services (as well as other professions, such as teachers) are facing a professional *identity crisis*. If the work of a doctor is thought of as a balance between the two poles of therapy and teaching, then today in the West the balance needs to move towards the pole of teaching. 'Doctor' means teacher. From those who work in Community Therapy Units we gain further insight into this understanding of the doctor as teacher: both patient and doctor work together as learners, each with their own contribution to make. The move towards teaching involves a change in the nature of the professional authority to be exercised. Both nurse and social worker need to be given more responsibility and to work as colleagues with doctors rather than as aides. Practice nurses in this country and medical auxiliaries in other countries are first steps in the right direction.

3. *Education for health* is not simply an extra discipline similar to other clinical subjects. It is what health and illness are all about within the movement of man towards greatness. The first

health educators in society are mothers of families. There are also those whom Caplan[140] calls 'culture carriers': they are key people in the local life of street and town, whose conversation and attitudes shape public opinion. Such people would be important in changing attitudes to health, illness and death. Their education and support could be an important part of a doctor's role.

As well as laity, professionals like doctors, nurses, health visitors, social workers, speech therapists, radiographers, dieticians and teachers are educating others constantly about health both directly and indirectly. It is not so much a matter of seeking special opportunities as of making the right use of existing contacts with pupils, clients and patients. In education for health we are learning together with other people; rather than instructing the ignorant.

In teaching sex at school, for example, there are certainly biological facts about sexual intercourse to be conveyed, but such information should not be given as if it was only a functional skill to be acquired, rather than an intimate way of conversation (verbal and non-verbal) within the context of a growing relationship. In speaking of this wider context, pupils and teachers are learners together. There is never a point in the study of human relations where we 'know it all'.

The many volunteers in hospital and in the social services in the community can influence attitudes to health in their neighbourhood. It could be part of policy to 'train' too many and deliberately to return (as it were) some of them to their local communities as more careful neighbours.

It is suggested that the primary task of the hospital is to enable patients, their families and staff, to learn from the experience of illness and death how to build a healthy society. To take learning seriously in hospital could mean making provision in the ward area for groups of patients, families and staff to meet and to converse together, about cancer, death, family planning, etc. and how to live more fully in the light of their experience. Some sessions could be planned and some open.

4. *Primary care of patients in the community.* Because so much illness in the West is emotional, and has family and social roots, it is questioned whether our general practitioner should be primarily a medical man trained in hospital medicine. The need is for a man or woman with much more social understanding

103

who is well versed in human behaviour: someone with a more general doctor/nurse/social work type of training. It is possible that the knowledge and skills required are too great for an individual, and that the general practitioner should be a troika of nurse, doctor and social worker. Leadership would not necessarily rest always with the doctor: this is a situation derived from the clinical model of health.

Medical education needs to be directed to the education of general practitioners, with a spin off into hospital medicine: not, as at present, to the education of hospital doctors with a spin off into general practice.

The primary assessors of illness are patients themselves, mothers of families, relatives, friends and neighbours. Patients could be educated to take more responsibility for themselves and their families. In certain conditions such as diabetes and asthma this is already done, and this could be extended by suitable research. There is no reason why people should be treated as patients just because they want help with family planning.

Already there is a steady movement towards giving patients care in their homes rather than in hospital. Support services in the home like home helps and district nurses need to be given much higher priority for funds. Birth and death need to be seen less as clinical events, and more as family events. This would have consequences in terms of domiciliary services, buildings and professional training.

5. *Health Planning* is not just the responsibility of the professions who work to keep us well, but belongs widely to society. To discuss health there must be present, in addition to doctors and nurses, housewives, artists, ministers of religion, teachers, environmentalists, architects, industrialists, economists and so on. Within this context hospital medicine can be a good servant so long as it does not dominate policy-making. Health is a political matter.

The function of the NHS in providing intelligence for the nation about what is going wrong in its life (e.g. a rising incidence of stress and alcoholism) may, in the long run, be more important than its executive function of treating diseases which may be important symptoms of social disease. There is an opportunity for the newly appointed Community Health Councils to become architects of social health. In particular they give the public a voice, and have an important social educational role.

There is at present a sequence of changes going on in the method of providing health care. This is most noticeable in the third world as its peoples escape from Western patterns of thought. Hospital medicine is giving ground to preventive medicine: preventive medicine is giving ground to community development. The importance of the last-mentioned is that it takes seriously the human (Abraham) factors which are related to health: for example, involvement of rather small groups of people on a local scale, respect for the people's own wishes (such as the need to grow more food before building a clinic), the gift of responsibility to the people (experts in consultative roles), and the possibility of sharing in decisions. No one who is aware of the 'apathy culture' in many great cities will underestimate the difficulty of this.

In community development, because resources are limited, value choices must be made and priorities settled. Without a religious basis it is difficult to make ethical choices except on the basis of expediency.

The beauty of the environment, conservation and facilities for recreation are important elements in health planning.

6. *Buildings.* Beliefs shape buildings and buildings shape beliefs. There are and have been very different designs for health centres according to the ideas about health which their builders held. More consultation is needed with people locally to discover what they would wish.

The disadvantages of large hospitals are becoming apparent and experiments with community hospitals need to be extended. A continuing care unit[77] provides a much more person-centred type of service.

Much illness in Western society today is unsuitable for treatment in hospitals which are designed to serve best those with acute episodes.

Imaginative designs can help to shape the attitudes of those who use the buildings. There is every reason why health centres should be more convivial.

7. *Research.* We need to divert funds for research from the study of disease to the study of health. The concept of morale is closely related to ideas about mental health. Styles of leadership in expeditions for exploration or mountaineering, in army and

police units, in sports and mining teams, etc. are highly relevant to our understanding of health. Stress in modern life may make or break individuals, families or nations. We need to know more about how people's threshold for withstanding stress can be raised.

Aggression is an important part of our human make-up There are socially acceptable and unacceptable ways of expressing and using aggression. At present perhaps too many people have too much investment in expressing aggression through vicarious watching of football. The fruits of research into this kind of thing need feeding back into education so that we educate children for manhood and womanhood—not just manpower.

The concepts of quality are not well understood: we need more research into the relationship between man and his environment, between soil and food and vitality.

8. *Ethics.* Because our resources are limited, choices of value have to be made between one service or another; between (perhaps) extended services for old people and a full family planning service. On what basis do we make such choices? Clinical facts, religious values, political practicalities or expediency? While doctors in the West are concerned about ethical questions such as euthanasia, in vitro fertilisation, A.I.D. and genetic counselling, the public are more concerned about questions such as 'the one or the many' (whether scarce resources of money, equipment and personnel should be used in saving rather few lives or be spread more widely for the comfort of a greater number of people with less critical illness): or whether it is not more creative of family health to have normal babies at home? And is clinical cure really the highest priority of a hospital? Or whether we should not strive to provide basic food and housing for all men everywhere *first*, before we provide luxuries for the few (here I am expressing a question for millions the world over—the greater public). And if you choose to become a doctor, whether you serve humanity where there are already plenty of doctors or where there is a desperate need for more. Professions who have to make such choices need to learn, as a normal part of their professional education, how men and women down the ages have made ethical decisions. We need some professorships and lectureships in some such subjects as 'Health and Human Values'.

This summary of practical conclusions clearly indicates that I do not look for some simple single-thrust solution to a complex crisis in our understanding of health. We require a new sense of direction at many points simultaneously. Whatever situation we are considering, to speak of health always enlarges the context.

Recently the Duke of Edinburgh[141] speaking in Australia said:

> Until it can be demonstrated that science, technology and economic growth can take the place of religion and provide that essential inspiration and motive which has created all great civilisations in the past, it would appear that our culture is simply free-wheeling on our Christian inheritance. . . . The very essence of most religions . . . is that they provide the only satisfactory alternative to expediency in making judgements and decisions on the important issues which each generation has to face.

Health is . . .

Throughout the book we have made descriptions of what health appeared to be like in different situations and from different viewpoints. Consistently it has appeared as a dynamic conception, enlarging the context of whatever situation we were studying with devastatingly practical implications for a culture hell-bent on narrowing contexts.

A collection of some of the most important sentences about health now follows. Its purpose is partly that of an index, partly that of a summary, and partly as an aid to reflection.

p. 2   Health is a positive quality of well-being.

p. 2   Health was not just perfection, but a practical notion related to function.

p. 6   Health is symptomatic of a correct relationship between man and his environment: his supernatural environment, the world around him, and his fellow man. . . . Health is associated with good, blessing and beauty—all that is positively valued in life. (Navaho concept).

after the European pattern but through the enhancement of their own cultural life. Health is perhaps the social milieu which enables each member, individually and jointly, to become more fully human.

pp. 43/4 The re-discovery of the importance of inter-personal factors in the promotion of health has brought together the ideas of 'health' and 'persons living together in harmony'.

p. 44 Health is interpersonal.

p. 45 Mental health is not a viable concept apart from bodily health.

p. 45 Psychiatrists have introduced a new cluster of criteria for the evaluation of individual and social well-being with profound effects on our ideas of health. We must now include interpersonal factors such as acceptance or prejudice, ability to adapt to social change, attitudes to old age and death, and the stability of marriage and family life in our evaluation of the health of a society. These criteria can be seen to contain ethical assumptions.

p. 45 Psychiatrists, by introducing interpersonal factors into medicine, have brought the concept of love into health.

p. 47 Our understanding of ways of life as sickness-producing or health-enhancing.

pp. 50/1 It could be that the search for a friend ... is not simply a search for care and relief from anxiety, depression and the symptoms of alienation and loss of identity so rife in Britain, but a search for meaning, for quality of life, for values other than materialist, and for a chance to develop our humanity together, in fact a search for health.

p. 55 There is no way to health through the cure of illness. Indeed we can no longer maintain the old *clinical* distinction between 'wellness' and 'illness' upon which the Health Service is based. Rather than trying to reach health by understanding illness, we must first try to understand health, in the light of which we may be able to say something about being well or ill.

p. 55 Health is situational, that is, it is related to what a people believes to be fullness of life for them. It is an expression of qualities to which they give value, and because they must choose between different factors in a world of limited resources, ethico/political decisions are in-involved. Health is evaluated by many criteria drawn from every corner of a people's life, including their capacity for enriching interpersonal relationships.

p. 58   Aggrey points to the heart of health as possibility.

p. 58   Health is an adventure.

p. 59   Health is concerned with a different set of factors related to humanness, to human relations in community. These factors which make for health are comparable to Hertzberg's 'motivators' and are concerned with a sense of personal and social identity, human worth, communication, participation in the making of political decisions, celebration and responsibility.

p. 60   Hygiene is related to the basic necessities of biological life. Health points to our human potential measured in terms of quality of life, individual, national and international. Health is a word related to the quality of human life in ecological terms, that is, it is not just an individual quality, but is related to life lived together in harmony with the environment. Hygiene is therefore a foundation for other qualities of life.

It is clear therefore that health is complex, and no single definition can serve our purpose. Only manifold descriptions can do justice to its richness.

p. 60   The language of science alone is insufficient to describe health: the languages of story, myth and poetry also disclose its truth. Any conference on health must be as widely representative of human genius as possible. Health is a symbolic word (in the sense of 'bringing together'): we cannot understand health by analysing it (breaking it down) only by building its different facets together. Health is then found to be a greater whole than the simple sum of its parts. An abstract definition may not be possible, but we can recognise health when we see it.

pp. 61/2 Giving men what they require does not necessarily bring health.

p. 62   To share my loaf with my brother is to acknowledge his body's hunger as equal to my own: it is also to confirm the reality of his brotherhood to me, and to show that I value his destiny as I value my own. This is health for us both. But it depends upon having a loaf to share—by which I mean that health is solidly related to material things. Man may not be able to live by bread alone, but he clearly cannot exist without it.

pp. 62/3   To argue that health is more than meeting basic human necessities for food and clothing and shelter, is not to devalue these basic necessities. It is in fact to suggest that the material necessities of life—biologically essential for our very existence—can be a further means of enhancing our humanness.

p. 63   We do not compete for health in the way we compete for hygiene. Health is not for the rich to give to the poor. Health is a quality of life they make together. Neither can possess health apart from the other, nor one steal health from the other without robbing himself. Rich and poor, doctor and patient, oppressor and oppressed make one another healthy or unhealthy. Health is non-competitive.

p. 63   In sharing my loaf with another I may meet not only his hunger for food but also his hunger for a brother. Health is about sharing, sharing what we have with one another, and sharing ourselves with one another. Health is about our relationship to material things, and our relationship to one another. We make health possible for one another.

p. 65   The whole-hearted acceptance of death is essential for health, both personal and social.

p. 66   In life there are patterns of death (spiritual death, death of quality) which are an ending or diminishment of health rather than an ending or diminishment of length of life.

p. 67   Inclusion is a pattern of health, *exclusion* a pattern of death (the leper).

p. 67   So society excludes (kills, sometimes literally) either by its attitudes, by segregation, institutionalisation or execution, the bad, the mad, the black, the widow, the leper, the aged, the underprivileged, the mentally subnormal, the rebel and the dying. This exclusive pattern of dealing with 'pollution' results in a 'safe' and sanitated society, but not a healthy society.

p. 68   He was independent enough to defy those who sincerely sought to save his life, because he had found something greater to give his life to, rather than merely prolonging it.

p. 69   This affirmation of African dignity is health. In health, difference is an enrichment, and a healthy community would include both black and white men; unafraid perhaps to acknowledge their prejudice and their differences because made of one blood. We would recognise that what we share in common as men and women is far greater than our differences which then appear as an enrichment, not a source of division. Health is inclusive.

p. 71   Not until we have accepted death and discovered life to be dominant over it, are we free to think and speak and act out of love for life and health, rather than attacking defects which are unconsciously feared as foretastes of physical death.

p. 72   In Europe widespread loss of Christian belief has resulted in a fear of death which has drained the word 'health' of its truly human dimension. Because our model of health is shaped by fear of biological death, cure of disease naturally becomes a supreme value: resources for the support and prolongation of life the supreme concern.

p. 72   To become a Christian is not to be separated from other men, but to become aware of our unity with all creation and the family of MAN in a new way. It is to become willing to affirm as my brother and to give my life daily—even unto death—for any man be he/she young or old, healthy or sick, Christian or not, good, bad, white, mad, black, stranger or trusted friend. This is life and health, its denial is death.

p. 73   The man who leads his family, his party, his Church, his profession, or his nation into healthier styles of life brings them to the test. The risk of life and the risk of death are fellow journeymen. It is here that the idea of morale is a helpful one because it presents health in a different way.

p. 74   A commanding officer faced with a rising sickness rate in his unit, will give first attention to the factors concerned with morale. He is working with a different idea of what constitutes a healthy unit and how you achieve health. If he worked to the medical idea of wellness he would ask for more doctors, more nurses, and an extra wing for the sick bay!—a completely different approach to the nature of illness and health.

p. 74 A healthy group of people can tolerate stress: that is, they are prepared to suffer. *Health does not exclude suffering.*

p. 76 The health of a family, a group, or a people depends upon the sharing of feelings of anxiety and guilt as well as joy and acceptance.

p. 77 Health positively includes suffering as a creative way of dealing with hostile and destructive feelings.

p. 77 That is a paradox at the heart of health. We work for health, but cannot attain it unless we are ready to risk its loss for the sake of one another.

pp. 79/80 Enough hygiene still does not guarantee health, although a willingness to share resources would in itself be a sign of health. We speak of 'underdeveloped' countries, by which we mean nations which have not achieved industrial development leading to wealth, wellness and longevity. But the word underdevelopment tells us little about the health and quality of life in those societies.

p. 80 Health is the milieu (human and environmental) which enables people individually and socially to grow towards fullness of life . . . To use the word 'towards' reminds us that men look forward to an ideal. . . . A vision of fullness of human life is essential to inspire us to build a healthy society now in a world where men are sick and resources are limited.

p. 81 Perhaps health like happiness is a surprising gift, not just an achievement.

p. 81 There are different assumptions about good and evil in what we have written about health. We have described a concept of health closely related to a people's culture and to the way in which they see 'the good life' and strive to obtain it. Implicit in such a vision is an attitude towards what is seen to be bad and harmful, and how to prevent, avoid, change or destroy it.

p. 83   This way towards health, which assumes that badness is not something which can be externalised and projected, is powerfully presented in the crucifixion and resurrection of Jesus. . . . It is this way towards health through suffering which is denied in Western culture today.

p. 83   Those who think and act in accordance with these different schemata, perceive 'badness' in different ways, and accordingly seek different ways towards the good life. It is different attitudes like this which mould a people's ideas of health and direct their search towards it.

p. 84   . . . the decisive influence of a people's beliefs about good and evil, in the formation of their concept of health and of the way they set out to achieve it. Such beliefs, often unexamined but tenaciously held, have far-reaching consequences in terms of health care and social services, professional training and design of buildings.

p. 85   Our beliefs about the nature of health and how we develop towards a healthy society, affect the design of buildings, the style and training of professions and the order of priorities for the allocation of resources, both money and manpower. Beliefs have expensive consequences.

p. 86   Health cannot be understood by analysis, but only through a kind of building process. Health is like a married couple.

p. 86   Health is always that further possibility in human life to which experience, encouragement or friendship may point. Health makes sense of the work of the NHS and other hygiene factors such as education, agriculture and housing. Health is the wider context within which medicine, teaching and politics are practised.

p. 90   It is essential that these lay councils see their role as concerned with the promotion of health and not the eradication of illness. We have made an important distinction between hygiene and health (diagram 9). What is commonly referred to as Comprehensive *Health* Planning is primarily concerned with the provision of *hygiene*, with meeting man's biological requirements—his Adam needs. It is important to give proper attention to such basic essentials for living. But health relates to further human possibilities (man's Abraham needs) for responsibility, sharing in local political decisions, communication, celebration and interpersonal relationships. It is equally important to give proper attention to these further factors which have an important influence on social morale and which may make quality of life possible.

p. 90   Doctors are authoritative on the subject of illness, but in matters of health carry the same authority as, for example, teachers, mothers and environmentalists.

p. 90   It is the members of a society who must say what they mean by health (there are no health specialists) and must make the ethical and political choices involved.

p. 92   The Peckham Health Centre . . . was a centre for family, not individual membership. . . . The medical laboratory visibly subserved the main purpose of the Centre which was health.

p. 93   The modern Health Centres are polyclinics shaped by the belief that we achieve health by the prevention, diagnosis and treatment of disease. The buildings shape the beliefs of those who grow up with them and the language of illness becomes their language, until it can actually be difficult, as in Britain today, to speak of health in any other way.

p. 93   The Peckham Health Centre and the Health Centres of the 1970s are built on different beliefs about what health is and how you work towards it.

p. 94   The primary task of a hospital can be described as: To enable patients, their families and staff to learn from the experience of illness and death how to build a healthy society.

p. 94   In hospital—particularly teaching hospitals—the medical model of health is powerfully operant, conditioning men's attitudes and beliefs. We must take seriously this influence of the hospital as a living learning arena, for today it is working against health.

p. 95   One of the basic differences in this unit (the Thayer hospital) is the way in which staff understand health and disease in terms of man's adaptation to his environment. This shifts the whole emphasis of their work from disease to people. The model of health underlying the work is a functional one, and the style of medicine to which this gives rise is different.

p. 95   The continuing care unit is consciously used as a 'living learning arena' in which education is important. Matters of individual and family morale are given attention. Health is understood more in terms of the response or adaptation of individuals and their families to a particular situation. Much thought is given to ways in which a person's capacity for active life can be maximised, and his disability overcome.

p. 96   It is at the point where an illness is relatively unshaped either by doctor or patient that the patient may be encouraged to respond healthily to sickness.

p. 101   Health may appear in or through illness and suffering. Illness may be a learning experience. A leper settlement may be a healthy community. A hospital ward may likewise be healthy or sick. The possibility of health in these situations depends upon people, professional or lay, who promote the further possibility of health. Nurses, doctors or patients may be creators or destroyers of health among themselves or others. The health of a ward may stem from the influence of a patient, a nurse or a domestic cleaner.

p. 101   In the community at large there are key people who promote health or illness.

p. 101   Every community has its key people who listen to, advise and help their neighbours, colleagues or chance acquaintances. They are the kind of people to whom others turn in a crisis. They are the carriers of a society's culture and therefore the actual builders or destroyers of health. . . . They can be the salt that brings out the flavour of a people's life together.

Reflections

Health is a concept like truth which cannot be defined. To define it is to kill it.

Nor can it be possessed. It can only be shared. There is no health for me without my brother. There is no health for Britain without Bangladesh.

Health is like an unknown territory which we must explore and describe from within. Its secrets are denied to those who view it only from outside.

Man's vision of his wholeness constantly 'breaks the shell of his understanding', disturbs his complacency, and tempts him to new adventures beyond the next ridge. Better to starve as an eagle than to exist as a plump chicken.

Like happiness there is an element of unconsciousness about health. When you know you are healthy you are not.

Health cannot be ensured. Like love and truth 'it resents approaches that are too intense'. We can only pay attention to the things which make health possible. Health comes as a surprise. The guest, whose room has been prepared, arrives: but unexpectedly. Health is a gift, a grace.

Health always enlarges the context of whatever situation we are considering. As a grain of sand reflects the cosmos, health reflects wholeness. Health is a foretaste of wholeness to come. Health is both great in conception and detailed in practice. It must answer to the pull of both vision and action: of both the 'not yet' of the future and the 'now' of the present. Health therefore contains sorrow: the sorrow of not being whole.

In the West our conception of health has diminished: we suffer from poverty of vision but not lack of skills. Health is dead: but long live health. Health is now being reborn as an explosive vision with disturbing consequences for the Western style of life. Health is an idea whose time has come.

Health widens every context including its own. Healthy—what for? For fullness of life, for fullness of humanity. For what? Health raises the ultimate question of man himself and of God.

What does it mean to be sorrowful yet always rejoicing, to be healthy when disabled or dying? Augustine wrote:[142]

'Our hearts are restless until they find their rest in Thee.'

Health has this quality of restlessness. It could be that our search for health is the secular mould in which our search for God is cast. We do not find 'God-talk' meaningful, and 'holiness' is sadly devalued. So we speak of our search in a different language, the language of health. But we are betrayed. For our Western conception of health is hollow. We have discerned death as the enemy, but have mistaken his shape. Natural death is the friend of man. We can but stave off his untimely arrival.

But the death of quality, whose shape is meaninglessness, whose terror is aloneness, and whose sting is dehumanisation, we hardly dare to recognise in ourselves. The splendid weapons of medicine and surgery with which we try to keep death at bay, are inappropriate here. They bring us wellness, and for this our appetite is ravenous though perverted. We are already well enough. We exist long enough.

In the struggle for health—for meaning, for community and for fuller humanity—the tools are different. If health is a gift we need not only to strive but also to listen, to bear, to wait, to wonder and to worship. We are what we receive.

Health does not exist as a present contentment but in our restlessness. We do not ask a child why he is dancing. We dance too. And we live to dance another day faster and more furiously.

Healthy for what? For God. For that which is at the heart of all that is, in which we live and move and have our being. For the ultimate Context.

The experience of health, because it is a foretaste of wholeness to come, contains, like beauty, love and joy, the answer in itself.

For what are we healthy? Just for the fun of it!

References

PART I

1. G. Orwell, *Nineteen Eighty Four* (Penguin), 1954
2. *A Health Service for Milton Keynes* (Dept. of Health and Welfare, Aylesbury), 1968, p. 14
3. Richard Crossman, *The Future Structure of the National Health Service* (H.M.S.O.), 1970, Foreword
4. The title of a sociological study of institutions for the mentally retarded: Pauline Morris, *Put Away* (Routledge & Kegan Paul), 1969
5. Personal communication from a doctor
6. M. A. H. Melinsky, 'Widows in Society', in *Good Grief*, papers from a conference of the Institute of Religion and Medicine (St. Mary Abchurch Vestry, Abchurch Lane, London, EC4N 7BA), 1970, p. 3
7. Cruse Clubs, Charter House, Lion Gate Gardens, Richmond, Surrey
8. Margaret Read, *Culture, Health and Disease* (Tavistock), 1966, p. 25
9. *On the State of the Public Health*, Annual Report of the Chief Medical Officer, D.H.S.S. (H.M.S.O.—London), 1973
10. *Epilepsy in Society* (Office of Health Economics, 162 Regent Street, London, W1R 6DD), 1971
11. J. Mathers, 'Psychiatry and Religion', in *Religion and Medicine I*, ed. M. A. H. Melinsky (S.C.M.), 1970, p. 9
12. M. Wilson, *The Hospital—a place of Truth* (Institute for the Study of Worship and Religious Architecture, University of Birmingham), 1971, pp. 22 ff
13. R. L. Coser, 'Alienation and Social Structure', in *The Hospital and Modern Society*, ed. B. Friedson (Collier-Macmillan), 1963, p. 231
14. F. Stockwell, *The Unpopular Patient* (Royal College of Nursing), Research Project Series 1, No. 2, pp. 54, 58
15. R. King, N. Raynes and J. Tizard, *Patterns of Residential Care*, International Library of Sociology and Social Reconstruction (Routledge & Kegan Paul), 1971
16. J. Mathers, 'Custodial or Residential Care for the Long-stay patient?', *The Lancet*, April 22, 1972, pp. 894–5

17. A. K. Rice, *The Enterprise and its Environment* (Tavistock), 1963, p. 253

18. F. Stockwell, *The Unpopular Patient* (see ref. No. 14), Chapter 13 pp. 69 ff

19. M. Wilson, 'Communicating a bad prognosis', *General Practitioner* December 3, 1971, p. 17

20. P. Speck, 'The Hospital Visitor', *Nursing Times*, 69, 27, July 5, 1973 p. 878

21. John Bowlby, *Child Care and the Growth of Love* (Pelican), 1953

22. Mary Ainsworth, *Maternal Deprivation—a reassessment* (W.H.O.-H.M.S.O.), 1962

23. M. Wilson, *The Hospital—a Place of Truth* (see ref. No. 12), pp. 103–4

24. M. L. J. Abercrombie, *The Anatomy of Judgement* (Pelican), 1969

25. I. Illich, 'In praise of Conviviality', *The Listener*, December 16, 1971, Vol. 86, No. 2229, p. 827

26. The Cassel Hospital, Ham Common, Richmond, Surrey

27. R. Kemp, 'Our Obsession with the hospital', *British Journal of Hospital Medicine*, Vol. 2, No. 11, November, 1969, p. 1877

28. R. A. Lambourne, 'Towards an Understanding of Medico-Theological Dialogue', in *Religion and Medicine II*, ed. M. A. H. Melinsky (S.C.M.), 1973, p. 12

29. R. A. Lambourne, 'A Concepts Map of the Practice of Medicine', reproduced in the above paper (No. 28), p. 18.

30. D. H. Meadows, D. L. Meadows, J. Randers and W. W. Behrens III, *The Limits to Growth* (Potomac Associates' Book, Earth Island Ltd., London), 1972, p. 19

31. J. H. Bryant, *Health and the Developing World* (Cornell University Press, New York), 1969, Preface

32. D. Morley, Personal communication quoted by M. King, see following reference (No. 33)

33. M. King, 'Medicine in Red and Blue', *The Lancet*, 1972, Vol. 1, No. 7752, p. 679

34. R. A. Lambourne, 'Models of Health and Salvation, Secular and Christian', *Study Encounter* (World Council of Churches), Vol. VII, No. 1, 1971, item SE/01, p. 4

35. *Ibid.*, p. 9

36. M. King, *Medical Care in Developing Countries* (Oxford University Press), 1966

37. D. Acheson, 'Southampton—Some First-year Experiences', *British Medical Journal*, 1972, 3, 166

38. H. E. Shortt and P. C. C. Garnham, Correspondence, *Nature*, 1948, Vol. 161, p. 126

39. For example:

(i) R. Lamerton, *Care of the Dying* (Priory Press), 1973

(ii) Monnica C. Stewart, *My Brother's Keeper?* (Health Horizon, London), 1968

40. J. Clark, *A Family Visitor* (Royal College of Nursing), 1973, see discussion in Chapter 10

41. M. Wilson, *The Hospital—a Place of Truth* (see ref. No. 12), pp. 114 ff

42. *Ibid.*, p. 154

43. *Ibid.*, p. 117

44. *Ibid.*, p. 117

45. Simone de Beauvoir, *Old Age* (Deutsch and Weidenfeld & Nicolson), 73

PART II

46. R. A. Lambourne, 'Mental Health, Christian Medical Mission and e future concept of Comprehensive Health Care', *Religion and Medicine II*, . M. A. H. Melinsky (S.C.M.), 1973, p. 25

47. *Ibid.*, pp. 25–7

48. *Ibid.*, p. 28. The diagram has been adapted

49. *Medical Care in Developing Countries* (Office of Health Economics, see f. No. 10), 1972, p. 26

50. *Ibid.*, p. 25

51. Office of Health Economics (see ref. No. 10)

52. T. A. M. Nash, *The Anchau Rural Development and Settlement Scheme* I.M.S.O.), 1948. (Abstracted in the *Tropical Diseases Bulletin*, 1949, 46, p. 229)

53. R. S. Arole, 'Comprehensive Rural Health Project—Jamkhed, dia', *Contact* (Christian Medical Commission, World Council of Churches),)72, No. 10

54. E. Abraham, E. G. Silassie *et al.*, *On the interrelation between proclamation the gospel and human development*, Addis Ababa, May 9, 1972, an open letter

55. J. R. Sibley, 'The Koje Do Project—Progress and Problems', *Contact* World Council of Churches), 1971, Occasional Paper No. 5

56. D. Morley, *Paediatric Priorities in the Developing World* (Butterworth),)73, Chapter 19

57. W. Smith and J. B. O'Donovan, 'The Practice Nurse—a New Look', *ritish Medical Journal*, December 12, 1970, 4, 673

58. Katherine Elliott, 'Using medical auxiliaries: some ideas and amples', *Health, Manpower and the medical auxiliary* (Intermediate Tech-ology Group, London), 1971, p. 29

59. M. H. King, *Medical Care in Developing Countries* (Oxford University ess), 1970

60. *Medical Care in Developing Countries* (Office of Health Economics, see f. No. 10), p. 29

61. R. A. Lambourne, 'Models of Health and Salvation, Secular and hristian', *Study Encounter* (see ref. No. 34), p. 3

62. J. Bowlby, *Child Care and the Growth of Love* (Pelican), 1953

63. E. Erikson, *Identity, Youth and Crisis* (Faber), 1968

64. R. A. Lambourne, 'Mental Health, Christian Medical Mission and ae future concept of Comprehensive Health Care' (see ref. No. 46), p. 31. he diagram has been adapted.

65. *Ibid.*, p. 30

66. *Matthew* 7, v. 9

67. (i) Prospects in Health (Office of Health Economics, see ref. No. 10), . 6

(ii) P. J. Taylor, 'Personal Factors associated with sickness absence', *ritish Journal of Industrial Medicine*, 1968, 25, 106

68. P. W. Warren, 'Sin and Insanity', *Theoria to Theory*, Vol. 4, Third Quarter, July, 1970, p. 43

69. C. S. Lewis, *The Great Divorce* (Fontana), 1971

70. M. Jones, *Social Psychiatry in Practice* (Pelican—first pub. Tavistock), 1952

71. 'Story of a short-stay patient in a Psychiatric Hospital', *Nursing Mirror*, November 22, 1968, p. 26

72. H. Green, *I never promised you a rose garden* (Pan), 1967

73. D. Martin, *Adventure in Psychiatry* (Bruno Cassirer), 1962, p. 43

74. J. S. Cox, 'Anxiety and Authority in a Therapeutic Community', *Religion and Medicine I*, ed. M. A. H. Melinsky (S.C.M.), 1970, p. 32

75. M. Siirala, *Medicine in Metamorphosis* (Tavistock), 1969

76. D. G. Langsley *et al.*, 'Family Crisis Therapy—Results and Implications', *Family Process*, September, 1968, 7, 2, pp. 145–8

77. H. Willard and S. V. Kasl, *Continuing Care in a Community Hospital* (Harvard University Press), 1973

PART III

78. Edwin Smith, *Aggrey of Africa* (S.C.M.), 1929, p. 136

79. *Luke* 4, v. 4

80. F. Hertzberg, *Work and the Nature of Man* (Staples Press), 1968

81. A. S. Maslow, *Motivation and Human Personality* (2nd edition, Harper & Row), 1970

82. *Medical Care in Developing Countries* (Office of Health Economics, see ref. No. 10), p. 25

83. Simone Weil, *Waiting on God* (Fontana), 1959, p. 97

84. N. Berdyaev, *The fate of man in the modern world* (Ann Arbor Paperbacks, University of Michigan), 1961, p. 124

85. *Judges* 4, v. 23

86. *Luke* 15, v. 24

87. D. Lack, *Evolutionary Theory and Christian Belief* (Methuen), 1957, p. 77

88. *Matthew* 4, v. 4

89. A. Kayper Mensah, 'Imports and Exports', in *Messages—Poems from Ghana*, ed. K. Awoonor and G. Adali-Mortty (Heinemann), 1971, p. 72

90. P. Freire, *Pedagogy of the Oppressed* (Penguin), 1972

91. 4th Editorial, *Sunday Express*, August 27, 1972, p. 16

92. J. Mathers, *The Nature of Prejudice* (ONE for Christian Renewal, c/o 9 Coniston Road, London, N10), April, 1974, Folder

93. Olivia N. Mukuna, 'Salvation as a Process of Humanisation versus Separate Development as a Process of Dehumanisation', *Unpublished Paper*, 1973

94. E. Smith, *Aggrey of Africa* (see ref. No. 78)

95. J. Taylor, 'The Final Choice', *C.M.S. News-Letter*, 1968, 312, pp. 4–5

96. A. Watts, *Behold the Spirit* (Vintage Books), 1971 edition, p. 109

97. *John* 15, v. 13

98. 1 *John* 3, v. 13

99. D. Hammarskjöld, *Markings* (Faber), 1964, p. 136

100. R. W. Revans,
    (i) 'Structures and Obstructions', in *Religion and Medicine I*, ed. M. A. H. Melinsky (S.C.M.), 1970, p. 93
    (ii) *Standards for Morale* (O.U.P.), 1964
    (iii) 'Management, Morale and Productivity', in *Proceedings of the National Industrial Safety Conference*, 1963, (RoSPA), London, p. 84

101. J. Macmurray, *Reason and Emotion* (Faber), 1935, p. 46

102. J. Taylor, 'On not solving the problem', *C.M.S. News-Letter*, 1971, 353

103. R. A. Lambourne, *Community, Church and Healing* (Darton Longman and Todd), 1963, p. 162

104. *Prospects in Health* (Office of Health Economics, see ref. No. 10), pp. 12 ff

105. E. F. Schumacher, *Small is Beautiful* (Blond and Briggs), 1973

106. R. A. Lambourne, *Le Christ et La Santé* (Le Centurion-Labor et Fides), 1972, p. 26

107. *Leviticus* 16

108. M. Wilson, 'Violence and Non-Violence in the Cure of Disease and the Healing of Patients', *The Christian Century*, 1970, 87, 24, p. 756

109. M. Wilson, *The Church is Healing* (S.C.M.), 1966, Chapter 4, pp. 84 ff

110. R. A. Lambourne, *Le Christ et La Santé* (see ref. No. 106), p. 27

PART IV

111. I. Illich, *Deschooling Society* (Calder and Boyars), 1971

112. M. C. Hardie, 'Practical Steps towards Comprehensive Health Planning', *Community Medicine* (T.H.C. Reprint No. 737), February 2, 1973, p. 328

113. J. H. Bryant, 'Moral Issues and Health Care', *Healing* (News Letter of the Christian Medical Council, 475 Riverside Drive, New York, N.Y. 10027), 1970, 7

114. K. Barnard, 'Comprehensive Health Planning—the state of the art', *Community Medicine* (T. H. C. Reprint No. 737), February 23, 1973, p. 376

115. P. Draper, 'Value Judgements in Health Planning', *Community Medicine* (T.H.C. Reprint No. 737), February 23, 1973, p. 372

116. A. Jay, 'The Corporation Tribe', *Corporation Man* (Jonathan Cape), 1972, Chapter 10 especially p. 106 ff

117. 'Editorial', *Community Medicine* (T.H.C. Reprint No. 737), February 2, 1973, p. 323

118. L. H. Crocker and I. H. Pearse, *The Peckham Experiment* (Sir Halley Stewart Trust Publication, Allen & Unwin), 1943

119. *Ibid.*, p. 137

120. T. Cull and A. Bird, 'Patient—doctor seminars', *Journal of the Royal College of General Practitioners*, 1974, 24, pp. 247–50

121. T. D. Hunter, 'Self-run Hospitals', *New Society*, September 14, 1967, pp. 356–8

122. R. A. Lambourne, 'Hospital Salt, Theological Savour and True Humanism', *Unpublished Paper*, given to the Consultation on Health and Salvation, Tubingen, 1967

123. M. Wilson, 'The Primary Task of the Hospital', *The Hospital*, 1970, 66, p. 346

124. R. King, N. Raynes and J. Tizard, *Patterns of Residential Care* (see ref. No. 15)

125. H. Willard and S. V. Kasl, *Continuing Care in a Community Hospital* (see ref. 77)

126. R. Lamerton, *Care of the Dying* (see ref. No. 39)

127. M. Balint, *The Doctor, his Patient and the Illness* (Pitman Medical), 1957

128. M. C. Hardie, 'Practical Steps towards Comprehensive Health Planning' (see ref. No. 112)

129. For example, L. H. Crocker and I. H. Pearse, *The Peckham Experiment* (see ref. No. 118), Chapter 6, p. 93

130. I. K. Zola, 'Pathways to the Doctor—from person to patient', *Social Science and Medicine I*, 1973, pp. 677–89

131. R. J. C. P. Pearson, quoted by M. Whitfield (see ref. No. 133)

132. M. E. J. Wadsworth, 'Planning with the Consumer in Mind', in *The Consumer and the Health Service*, ed. J. McKenzie (Office of Health Economics, see ref. No. 10), 1968, p. 21

133. M. Whitfield, 'The Pharmacist's Contribution to Medical Care', *Practitioner*, 200, March 1968, p. 434

134. A. Cartwright, *Patients and their Doctors* (Routledge & Kegan Paul), 1967, p. 196, Table 69

135. M. J. Field, *Search for Security* (Faber), 1960

136. *Medicine and Society* (Office of Health Economics, see ref. No. 10), 1972, p. 6

137. J. R. Ellis, 'Doctors of Tomorrow', *Twenty-four Talks* (King's Fund Hospital Centre), 1972, p. 45

138. W. Smith and J. B. O'Donovan, 'The Practice Nurse—a new look', *British Medical Journal* (see ref. No. 57)

139. M. Wilson, 'Violence and Non-violence in the Cure of Disease and the Healing of Patients', *The Christian Century* (see ref. No. 108)

140. G. Caplan, *An Approach to Community Mental Health* (Tavistock), 1961

141. H.R.H. the Duke of Edinburgh, 'Universities and the Diffusion of Culture', *Frontier*, 1974, 17, 3, p. 137

142. Augustine of Hippo, *The Confessions*, trans. E. B. Pusey (Everyman's Library—Nelson), Book 1, p. 1

Additional References

1. M. Lalonde, *A new Perspective on the Health of Canadians* (Govt. of Canada, Ottawa), 1974

This report describes a 'Health Field Concept', which considers Health under four headings: human biology, environment, life style and health care services. It is noted that most finance is devoted to the health care services for treatment of diseases arising under the other three headings. The report speaks of diseases due to overeating, smoking, and many accidents as 'diseases of choice'.

2. I. Illich, *Medical Nemesis* (Calder & Boyars), 1975

A book which studies the medicalisation of health from knowledge of North American culture. Like the present writer, Illich seeks a new model of health which takes seriously both individual and social life, pain, birth and death.

Index of Subjects

Index of Places

Index of Authors and Organisations

(Numbers refer to pages on which quotations and/or references occur)

133